Mary Henneberry

D1377901

Mary Henneberry

The Science of Movement

LESLIE BASFORD B.Sc.

FOUNDATIONS OF SCIENCE LIBRARY

GREYSTONE PRESS/NEW YORK · TORONTO · LONDON

CHIEF EDITORS

Leslie Basford, B.Sc.   Philip Kogan, M.Sc.

ASSISTANT EDITORS

Michael Dempsey, B.A., Michael Gabb, B.Sc., Clare Dover, B.Sc.
Cyril Parsons, B.Sc., Joan Pick, B.Sc., Michael Chinery, B.A.
David Larkin, B.Sc., Paul Drury Byrne, B.Sc.

CONSULTANT EDITORIAL BOARD

Sir Lawrence Bragg, M.C., O.B.E., F.R.S., M.A., Nobel Laureate

Sir James Chadwick, F.R.S., Ph.D., M.Sc., Nobel Laureate

Norman Fisher, M.A.

Sir Harry Melville, K.C.B., F.R.S., Ph.D., D.Sc.

Professor J. Z. Young, F.R.S., M.A.

This new presentation assembles freshly edited material from
'Understanding Science' on one subject into a single volume.

Copyright © MCMLXVI Sampson Low, Marston & Co. Ltd.

Library of Congress Catalog Card Number: 66-17975

Manufactured in U.S.A.

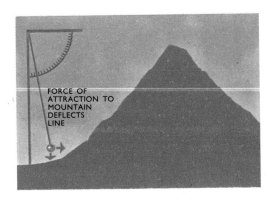

Contents

Forces and Equilibrium

CHAPTER ONE

Forces

IF a man wishes to shift a boulder, he has first to exert a *force*. Whenever a stationary body is set moving, it has first to be acted upon by a force. When it is in motion, its speed or its direction of motion may be changed, or it may be brought to rest, by using a force.

It is quite obvious that not only the *size* but the *direction* of a force is important. In fact, it is impossible to consider the effect of a force on a body

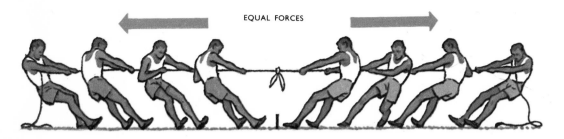

When each team exerts equal force on the rope, it remains still.

When one team exerts a bigger force than the other, the rope starts moving.

To stop the movement of the rope, the other team has to exert an extra force.

unless the direction of the force is known.

The best known force of all is the *force of gravity*. It pulls all bodies on the Earth's Surface towards the centre of the Earth. This force gives a body its *weight*. Force can be measured in *pounds weight* (lb. wt.) or *grams weight* (gm. wt.). This is the force that a standard pound or gram mass would experience under gravity, at the Earth's surface.

When we hold an object, such as a book, in our hands, we are withstanding the force of gravity. There is a force acting between the hands and the book that opposes the gravitational force. If the two forces cancel each other out exactly, the book will stand still. If the book were replaced by a lump of heavy metal, it might be that the hands and arms could not offer a sufficiently large opposing force to cancel out the force of gravity and the lump of metal would drop to the ground.

A similar thing happens in a tug of war. If each team is able to exert identical forces on the rope then neither side moves. If one side is able to give a bigger pull, then the weaker side is overcome and the whole

DOWNWARD FORCE OF GRAVITY

UPWARD FORCES EXERTED BY ARMS ON BOOKS

The arms are able to withstand the downward force exerted by the books by exerting an equal and opposite force. They are unable to do this when the man is holding a heavy box and he has to drop the box.

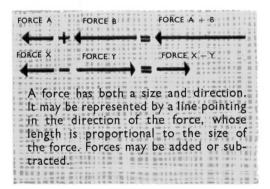

FORCE A · FORCE B · FORCE A + B

FORCE X · FORCE Y · FORCE X − Y

A force has both a size and direction. It may be represented by a line pointing in the direction of the force, whose length is proportional to the size of the force. Forces may be added or subtracted.

team is pulled forward. To stop the motion of both teams an extra force has to be exerted by the losing side. If the winning side were to start pulling at an angle to the original direction of the rope, then the direction of motion of both teams and the rope would change. In actual fact, the maximum effect is gained by pulling in the direction of the rope and not at an angle to it.

CHAPTER TWO

Moments

WHENEVER you push a door open, you apply a force to the door and the door rotates about its hinge. The *turning effect* of the force is called its *moment*. The place about which any object rotates, in this case, the hinge, is known as the *fulcrum*. If you push on a door as far away from the hinge as possible, it is very easy to push it open. Pushing near to the hinge, though, requires a large amount of effort. This is because a small force some distance away from the fulcrum can have the same *moment* as a large force near to the fulcrum.

The *moment* of a force is defined as the force multiplied by the perpendicular distance between the fulcrum and the line of action of the force. (Moment = force × distance). The units of moments are those of force and length, usually pounds-weight-feet or grams-weight-centimetres. For the boy on the seesaw the perpendicular distance between line of force and fulcrum is just the distance along the seesaw between fulcrum and boy. But for the boy on the bicycle the distance needed is not the six inch distance from the fulcrum to the boy's foot but is the shorter three

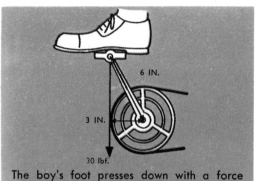

The boy's foot presses down with a force of thirty pounds weight. The *perpendicular* distance between the fulcrum and the line of force is three inches, not the six inches between the fulcrum and the pedal. The moment of the force is 30 lbf. × ¼ ft. = 7½ lbf. ft.

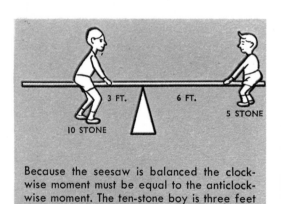

Because the seesaw is balanced the clockwise moment must be equal to the anticlockwise moment. The ten-stone boy is three feet away from the fulcrum and the five-stone boy, six feet away. The clockwise moment of 6×70 pounds force feet equals the anticlockwise moment of 3×40 pounds force feet.

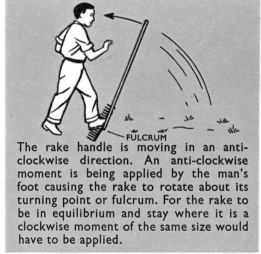

The rake handle is moving in an anticlockwise direction. An anti-clockwise moment is being applied by the man's foot causing the rake to rotate about its turning point or fulcrum. For the rake to be in equilibrium and stay where it is a clockwise moment of the same size would have to be applied.

inch distance from the fulcrum perpendicular to the line indicating the direction of the force.

The turning effect of a force which tends to turn an object in a clockwise direction is called a clockwise moment and the turning effect of an opposing force is called an anticlockwise moment. When the two moments exactly balance each other then the object is said to be in *equilibrium*. The simplest way of achieving equilibrium is to use two opposing moments of equal size, but it is quite possible to have one large moment balanced by several smaller moments. Here the sum of the smaller moments is equal in size to the larger moment. Equilibrium can also be attained by making *several* opposing moments balance each other. For the object to be in equilibrium the sum of the anticlockwise moments must be equal to the sum of the clockwise moments.

CHAPTER THREE

The Centre of Gravity

THE technique of high wire performing depends on the artist having a perfect sense of balance. Balance while moving on the ground is always very necessary but is something that seems to us to be automatic. Here balance is not difficult because the whole of the foot is in contact with the ground, but the circus performer has only a very small area of his foot in contact with the wire and this can readily provide a fulcrum or turning point about which he can rotate and fall if his balance is not perfect.

A small child when it is learning to walk often falls over because it has not yet learned the art of balancing. It leans too far forward and over it goes. It is extremely difficult but possible (in theory) to balance a pencil on its point if the pencil is absolutely vertical so that the weight of the pencil is directly above its point and is pressing down on it. If the pencil leans even slightly, its weight acts as if it is pressing down on one side of the point. This produces a turning effect or *moment*, and the pencil falls over (rotates about its point, the fulcrum).

It is true that every particle of every solid has weight but, for purposes of balancing, any object behaves as if

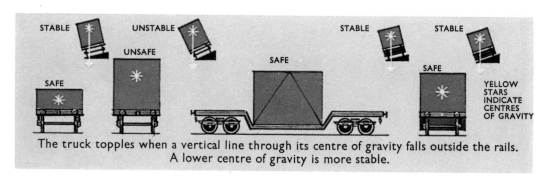

The truck topples when a vertical line through its centre of gravity falls outside the rails. A lower centre of gravity is more stable.

For the man to balance, his centre of gravity must be exactly above the wire.

Forces can produce moments or turning effects. The moment of a force is equal to the force multiplied by its perpendicular distance from the fulcrum. If the centre of gravity is directly above the fulcrum, then this perpendicular distance will be zero and so the moment or turning effect will be zero. The object will be in balance (equilibrium) no matter how heavy the object is. If the centre of gravity is not directly above the fulcrum, then a moment is produced. As there is no opposing moment to balance this the object is not in equilibrium and overbalances.

When someone balances on a tight-rope although he is in equilibrium, it takes only a small push to destroy this and push him off balance. In whichever direction he falls, his centre of gravity is bound to be lowered. In equilibrium the centre of gravity is at its highest point. This type of equilibrium is *unstable*.

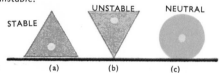

STABLE   UNSTABLE   NEUTRAL

(a)   (b)   (c)

Three types of equilibrium. (a) Stable: the centre of gravity is raised on tilting. (b) Unstable: on tilting, the centre of gravity is lowered. (c) Neutral: the centre of gravity does not change height.

For the equilibrium to be *stable*, i.e. the balance not easily destroyed, the object must be placed in such a way that if its position is disturbed, the centre of gravity will be raised. Then, the tendency is for the object to drop back into its original position.

If heavy weights are slung from the high wire bicycle so that they hang below the wire the centre of gravity of the system, bicycle, man and weights can be arranged to be below the wire. Any toppling movement of the bicycle will raise the centre of gravity. The tendency is for the bicycle to return to its original equilibrium position. The bicycle has been made much more stable.

Neutral equilibrium occurs when the centre of gravity of the object in equilibrium is neither raised nor lowered by disturbing the object. The centre of gravity of a cylinder on its side on a horizontal surface has its centre of gravity half way along the line through its centre. As the cylinder rolls over and over the centre of gravity remains at the same height.

Sometimes tight-rope walkers carry a long pole which acts as a fine centre of gravity adjustment. By having more pole on the right, then the centre of gravity is moved to the right and so on.

all its weight is concentrated at one point – its *centre of gravity*. If its centre of gravity is directly above the point of support then the object will balance; if it is not then it will over-balance. A tight-rope walker, while he is concentrating on keeping his balance is continuously ensuring that his centre of gravity is directly above the tight-rope.

FINDING THE CENTRE OF GRAVITY

It is quite easy to find the centre of gravity experimentally for an object such as a table tennis bat. The bat is hung in turn from three different points close to its edge. Each time, a plumb line (a piece of thin cord with a small heavy bob on the end) hangs freely from the same peg. As the centre of gravity of the plumb bob will always come to rest verti-

cally below the peg, the cord on which it hangs will be vertical. This cord is, therefore, used to mark a vertical line from the point of suspension. The centre of gravity of the bat will be somewhere on this line. When the bat has been hung from

The centre of gravity of the plank is at its mid-point, so it is easier to lift it in the middle than from one end.

CENTRE OF GRAVITY DIRECTLY BELOW POINT OF SUPPORT, SO NO TURNING EFFECT

TURNING EFFECT BECAUSE CENTRE OF GRAVITY IS NOT BELOW POINT OF SUPPORT

three different points, three lines will have been drawn on it. The point where these three lines cross is the centre of gravity.

As the centre of gravity of a framework, such as a chair, will most probably be in empty space, pencil marks cannot be used to mark the verticals. Instead, pieces of cord are tied across the framework so that they coincide with the three positions of the plumb line.

For more complicated objects like automobiles, the centres of gravity are usually found by calculation. Such objects are constructed from many uniform and regular objects (e.g. cubes and cylinders) whose centres of gravity are at their geometric centres. The turning effects (moments) of the various components about an imaginary line can be calculated easily, and the centre of gravity found.

To find the centre of gravity, the table tennis bat is hung from three points. The centre of gravity is where the lines cross.

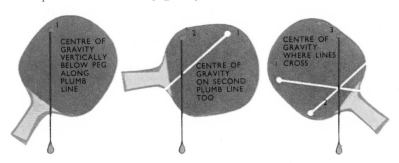

CENTRE OF GRAVITY VERTICALLY BELOW PEG ALONG PLUMB LINE

CENTRE OF GRAVITY ON SECOND PLUMB LINE TOO

CENTRE OF GRAVITY WHERE LINES CROSS

Simple Statics

WHEN an engineer designs a bridge or a building, he has to consider how the stresses in the various parts act on each other. Will the load exerted by the roof be too great for the girders to bear? Will the forces acting in one direction on a wall be greater than the forces acting in another? These questions and many other similar ones must be answered if the building is not to topple over.

The science of *mechanics* deals with the effect of forces on bodies, and is divided into two parts, *statics* and *dynamics*. Dynamics is the study of moving bodies, and statics the study of stationary bodies. The civil engineer, when he designs a building, has to

Friction exists between any two surfaces. By experiment it is found that the force of friction does not depend on the area of contact. It only depends on the weight downwards, and the nature of the two materials. The weight downwards is balanced by an equal and opposite reaction upwards. The law of friction states that when the body is on the point of slipping, *the force of friction = coefficient of friction × upwards reaction.*

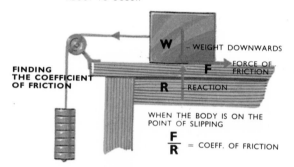

AS WEIGHTS ARE ADDED THE FRICTION BUILDS UP TO ITS MAXIMUM UNTIL SLIPPING IS JUST ABOUT TO OCCUR

FINDING THE COEFFICIENT OF FRICTION

W — WEIGHT DOWNWARDS

F — FORCE OF FRICTION

R — REACTION

WHEN THE BODY IS ON THE POINT OF SLIPPING

$\dfrac{F}{R}$ = COEFF. OF FRICTION

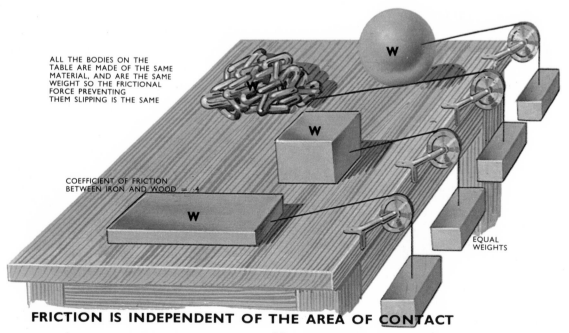

ALL THE BODIES ON THE TABLE ARE MADE OF THE SAME MATERIAL, AND ARE THE SAME WEIGHT SO THE FRICTIONAL FORCE PREVENTING THEM SLIPPING IS THE SAME

COEFFICIENT OF FRICTION BETWEEN IRON AND WOOD = ·4

EQUAL WEIGHTS

FRICTION IS INDEPENDENT OF THE AREA OF CONTACT

Various bodies in statical equilibrium. When a body is in equilibrium and does not move, its weight downwards must be balanced by an equal and opposite reaction upwards.

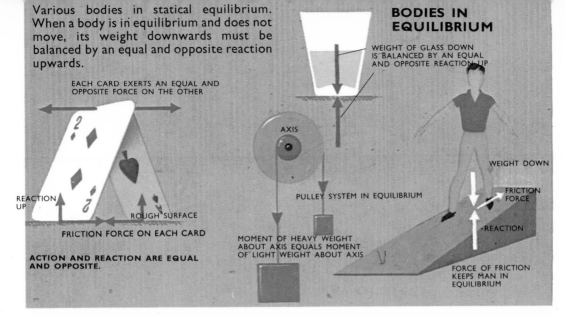

BODIES IN EQUILIBRIUM

WEIGHT OF GLASS DOWN IS BALANCED BY AN EQUAL AND OPPOSITE REACTION UP

EACH CARD EXERTS AN EQUAL AND OPPOSITE FORCE ON THE OTHER

AXIS

REACTION UP

ROUGH SURFACE

FRICTION FORCE ON EACH CARD

ACTION AND REACTION ARE EQUAL AND OPPOSITE.

PULLEY SYSTEM IN EQUILIBRIUM

MOMENT OF HEAVY WEIGHT ABOUT AXIS EQUALS MOMENT OF LIGHT WEIGHT ABOUT AXIS

WEIGHT DOWN

FRICTION FORCE

REACTION

FORCE OF FRICTION KEEPS MAN IN EQUILIBRIUM

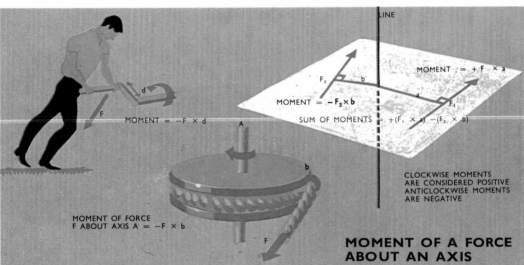

LINE

$MOMENT = +F \times a$

$MOMENT = -F_2 \times b$

F_2

b

a

F_1

SUM OF MOMENTS $= +(F_1 \times a) -(F_2 \times b)$

$MOMENT = -F \times d$

d

F

A

b

MOMENT OF FORCE F ABOUT AXIS A $= -F \times b$

F

CLOCKWISE MOMENTS ARE CONSIDERED POSITIVE ANTICLOCKWISE MOMENTS ARE NEGATIVE

MOMENT OF A FORCE ABOUT AN AXIS

A force besides its pushing or pulling effect has a turning effect. This is called its moment. The moment of a force about a line is the force $\times$ its perpendicular distance from the line.

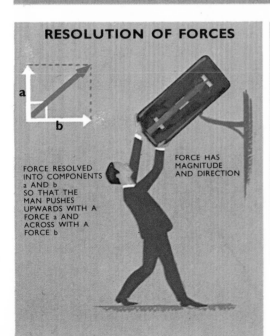

RESOLUTION OF FORCES

a

b

FORCE RESOLVED INTO COMPONENTS a AND b SO THAT THE MAN PUSHES UPWARDS WITH A FORCE a AND ACROSS WITH A FORCE b

FORCE HAS MAGNITUDE AND DIRECTION

Forces have direction and magnitude. From the parallelogram of forces it is seen that any force can be resolved into two components at right angles. To add two forces in different directions, it is only necessary to add or subtract the components.

ADDITION OF FORCES

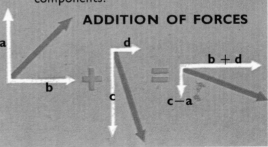

a

b

d

c

b + d

c – a

STATICS PROBLEM

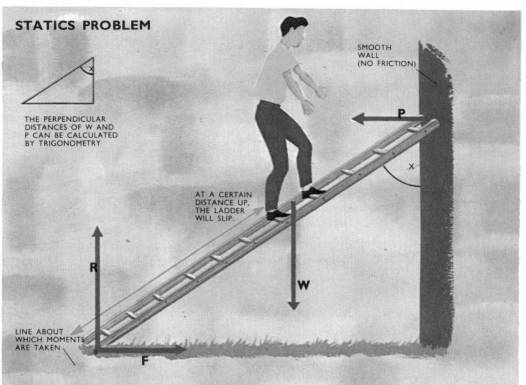

THE PERPENDICULAR DISTANCES OF W AND P CAN BE CALCULATED BY TRIGONOMETRY

SMOOTH WALL (NO FRICTION)

AT A CERTAIN DISTANCE UP, THE LADDER WILL SLIP.

P

W

R

F

LINE ABOUT WHICH MOMENTS ARE TAKEN

The problem is – how far up the ladder can the man go before it slips. This is an example of a typical problem in statics. To solve it, it is necessary to resolve forces and take moments i.e. to use the two conditions of statical equilibrium, which are:

The sum of the external forces (in any given direction) = 0.
The sum of moments of the external forces about *any* line = 0.

The external forces are drawn in R, W, F, P. In actual fact there will be some friction at the smooth wall but this is assumed negligible. To simplify the explanation the weight of the ladder has also been assumed negligible. Adding the external forces gives:

R − W = 0 in any vertical direction.
F − P = 0 in the horizontal direction.

The forces are already in parallel perpendicular directions so before adding there is no need to resolve them. W and P are in opposite directions to R and F so they have negative signs. From these two equations R = W, F = P.

To sum the moments, any line is chosen. Such a line would be that perpendicular to the plane of the page, through R and F. This line has the advantage that R and F have no moment about it, since they pass through it. The perpendicular distances from the line of the remaining external forces W and P are found, and the sum of their moments (which are in opposite directions) about this line written down. The top two equations, and the moment equation enable the problem to be solved.

think of a complicated system of forces – his problem is a gigantic exercise in statics. But quite simple problems like calculating the force exerted on a wall by a ladder have to be solved using exactly the same rules and methods.

The basic question to be asked is, under which conditions does a body re-

main stationary? The answer is that the body remains stationary if two conditions are fulfilled. The first condition is that all forces acting on the body must cancel each other out when their effect in any direction is found. All the forces are *resolved* in one direction and their values added together.

If the result is not zero, the body cannot be in equilibrium.

The second condition is that all the moments acting on a pivot must add up to zero. It is quite obvious that if the turning effect in one direction is greater than in another, the body cannot be in equilibrium – it will tend to spin around.

These two conditions add up to the simple rule for most problems in statics – *resolve forces and take moments.*

A ladder leans against a wall. A man starts to climb the ladder. As he goes up the ladder he moves nearer the point where the ladder might slip. How far up will he be when it does slip?

The forces are resolved first in the horizontal direction and then in the vertical. Then moments due to the forces acting on the ladder at its upper point of contact with the wall are found, and then at the lower. These calculations provide simple mathematical equations that can be solved to provide the answer.

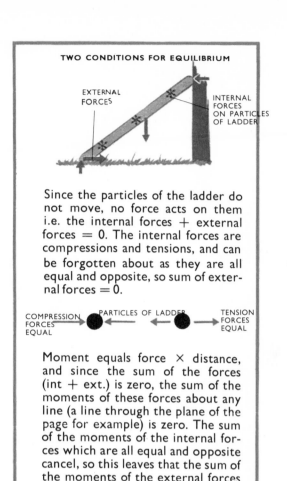

TWO CONDITIONS FOR EQUILIBRIUM

EXTERNAL FORCES

INTERNAL FORCES ON PARTICLES OF LADDER

Since the particles of the ladder do not move, no force acts on them i.e. the internal forces + external forces = 0. The internal forces are compressions and tensions, and can be forgotten about as they are all equal and opposite, so sum of external forces = 0.

COMPRESSION FORCES EQUAL

PARTICLES OF LADDER

TENSION FORCES EQUAL

Moment equals force × distance, and since the sum of the forces (int + ext.) is zero, the sum of the moments of these forces about any line (a line through the plane of the page for example) is zero. The sum of the moments of the internal forces which are all equal and opposite cancel, so this leaves that the sum of the moments of the external forces about any line = 0.

CHAPTER FIVE

Stress and Strain

WHEN a weight is hung from the end of a spring balance, the spring stretches. When the weight is taken off again, the spring goes back to its original length. The spring is said to be *elastic*. It stretches when it is pulled, and then springs back to its normal length when the pulling force is removed.

Stress is force per unit area. *Strain* is extension per unit length.

The spring balance is commonly used for weighing things, for the amount the spring stretches (the strain) is proportional to the weight attached (the stress). If the spring extends by one inch when a one pound weight is hung on it, then it will extend by two inches when a two pound weight is attached. If a book is hung from the end, and it extends the spring by three and a half inches, then the weight of the book must be three and a half pounds.

However, this will not always work. There is a limit to the amount of stress the spring can stand. If a heavier weight, for example a ten pound weight, is hung on the balance, then it may extend it by more than ten inches. The stress is no longer proportional to the strain. The spring has been weakened, and it now extends more easily.

If the weights are now taken off the spring, then the spring will probably go back to its original length. It has not lost any of its elasticity. But if more and more weights are piled on to the spring, it does not go back to its original length. It will be extended permanently. The spring has exceeded the *elastic limit*, and has lost some of its elasticity, or ability to spring back once the stress is removed. The spring may break if the weight hung from it greatly exceeds the elastic limit.

Spiral springs for spring balances are made of tempered steel wire – i.e. steel treated so that it is 'springy'. But it is not necessary to coil the wire into a spiral to get an elastic effect. A straight length of steel wire will stretch when it is pulled, and then spring back to its original length. The amount of stretching is very small, but it has applications in bridge-building, or steel frameworks for houses, where long lengths of metal will be subjected to various kinds of stress. The amount of strain, and the form it takes, will naturally be important. The simplest stresses and strains are the kinds involved when a straight length of wire is pulled along its length. The stresses and strains involved in spiral springs are more complicated.

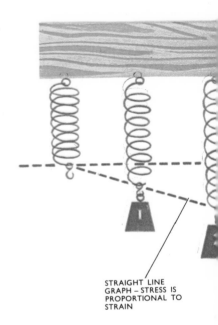

STRAIGHT LINE GRAPH – STRESS IS PROPORTIONAL TO STRAIN

Finding Young's Modulus

The conventional method of finding out how a length of wire behaves when it is stretched is to get a long length of wire, and pull it. The upper end of the wire is attached to a rigid beam in the ceiling, and weights are attached to the lower end. The extension of the wire, for various stresses, is measured. It is better to use a long length of wire than a shorter one, since the amount of stretching will be small, and a wire three feet long will

Material	Young's Modulus (in lbf. in²)
Copper	18,000,000
Steel	30,000,000
Tungsten	62,000,000
Soft, Vulcanized Rubber	about 300
Silk Fibre	1,000,000

obviously stretch three times as much as a wire one foot long. Special apparatus such as a *vernier* is often used to measure the extension accurately.

If successively heavier weights are hung on the wire, the extensions found in each instance, and the results are plotted on a graph, with stress along one axis and strain along the

for any one piece of wire. The constant ratio stress/strain is given the name *Young's modulus.*

If something has a high Young's modulus, then it does not stretch very much. For a large stress the strain (the fractional increase in length) is small. If something has a smaller Young's modulus, then a large stress is accom-

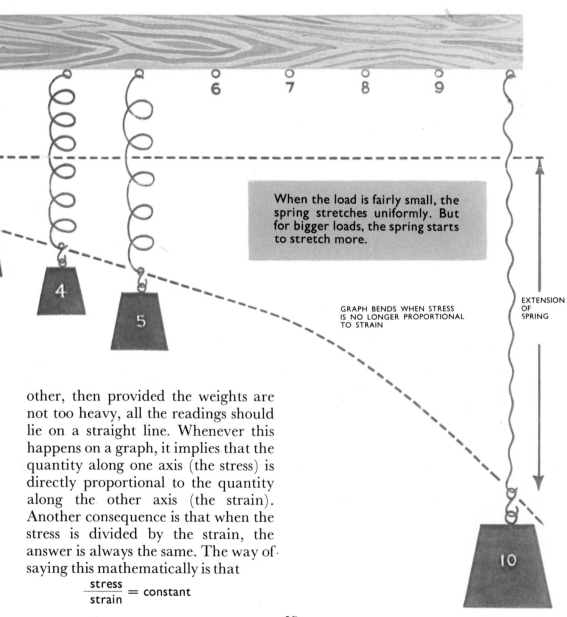

When the load is fairly small, the spring stretches uniformly. But for bigger loads, the spring starts to stretch more.

GRAPH BENDS WHEN STRESS IS NO LONGER PROPORTIONAL TO STRAIN

EXTENSION OF SPRING

other, then provided the weights are not too heavy, all the readings should lie on a straight line. Whenever this happens on a graph, it implies that the quantity along one axis (the stress) is directly proportional to the quantity along the other axis (the strain). Another consequence is that when the stress is divided by the strain, the answer is always the same. The way of saying this mathematically is that

$$\frac{\text{stress}}{\text{strain}} = \text{constant}$$

FINDING THE
LENGTH OF
THE WIRE

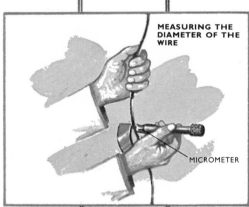

MEASURING THE
DIAMETER OF THE
WIRE

MICROMETER

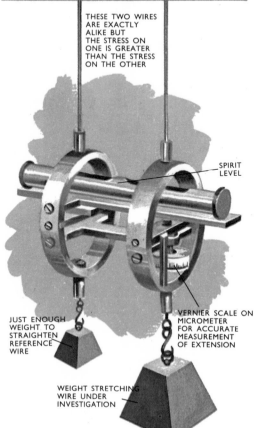

THESE TWO WIRES
ARE EXACTLY
ALIKE BUT
THE STRESS ON
ONE IS GREATER
THAN THE STRESS
ON THE OTHER

SPIRIT
LEVEL

JUST ENOUGH
WEIGHT TO
STRAIGHTEN
REFERENCE
WIRE

VERNIER SCALE ON
MICROMETER
FOR ACCURATE
MEASUREMENT
OF EXTENSION

WEIGHT STRETCHING
WIRE UNDER
INVESTIGATION

An experiment to find Young's modulus

The original length of the wire is 98·6 inches.

The diameter of the wire is 0·0949 inches, and so its area of cross-sections works out at 0·007068 square inches.

The extension is 0·014 inches, when the load on the wire is 30 lbf.

So Young's modulus for the wire is

$$\frac{stress}{strain} \quad or \quad \frac{force}{area} \div \frac{extension}{original\ length}$$

which is

$$\frac{30}{0·007068} \div \frac{0·014}{98·6}$$ lbs. weight per square

inch, or 29,900,000 lbs. weight per square inch.

panied by a large strain; the substance is more 'elastic'.

The two quantities 'stress' and 'strain' must be defined more exactly. The stress depends on the thickness of the wire. For if the *same weights* are hung on the ends of two wires of the same material, one thick and the other thin, the stress in the thicker wire is less than the stress in the thinner wire. The stretching force is spread out over a larger area. As a consequence, the thicker wire does not stretch as much as the thinner wire.

The most useful way in which the stress can be written is as *force per unit area*. If a 30 lb. force is hooked on to the end of a wire of cross-sectional area one thousandth of a square inch, then the stress is the force (in lbf.) divided by the cross-sectional area (in square inches), or

$$30 \div \frac{1}{1000}$$ lbf. per square inch.

On the other hand, the *strain* is always written as the extension in length per unit length. If this same wire is 100 inches long, and it stretches by one tenth of an inch, then the strain is equal to the extension divided by the original, unstretched length. Or

$$\text{strain} = \frac{1}{10} \div 100$$

In this example, Young's modulus, stress divided by strain, is equal to

$$\left(30 \div \frac{1}{1000}\right) \div \left(\frac{1}{10} \div 100\right) \text{ lbf. per square inch}$$

which is

$$30 \times \frac{1000}{1} \times \frac{10}{1} \times \frac{100}{1} \text{ lbf per square inch}$$

or 30,000,000 lbf. per square inch.

Once the stress and the strain have been expressed in standard units, the constructional engineer can easily work out the stresses and strains in a longer piece of wire of a much larger cross-sectional area.

The unit of Young's modulus may be expressed in units of pounds force per square inch, or in the metric system in Newtons (a unit of force) per square metre.

CHAPTER SIX

Torsion

WHEN drilling for oil, many thousands of feet of drill shafting are necessary for boring through overlying rock formations before the oil is reached. The whole length of shafts joined together is turned from the surface by a force – called a *torsional* or twisting force.

The resistance as the drilling head bites into the rock coupled with the turning force at the top causes the material of the long drill to become twisted up. It resists this twisting by means of its *torsional rigidity*. Some motor vehicles use torsion bar suspension for springing. One end of a bar is fixed and the other end is twisted by the uneven jolting of the vehicle. The twisted bar using its torsional rigidity acts as a spring.

The principles of torsion are used in many scientific instruments as a means of measuring small forces. In the moving coil galvanometer which measures electric current a coil hung by a fine fibre in a magnetic field is

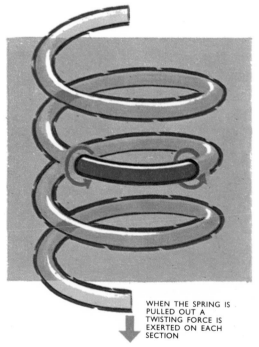

THE BACKWARD FORCE IN A SPIRAL SPRING IS PROPORTIONAL TO THE AMOUNT IT IS PULLED OUT. THIS IS CALLED HOOKES LAW, AND ALSO APPLIES TO ELASTIC BANDS

WHEN THE SPRING IS PULLED OUT A TWISTING FORCE IS EXERTED ON EACH SECTION

The torsion of the steel of a spring accounts for its elasticity.

19

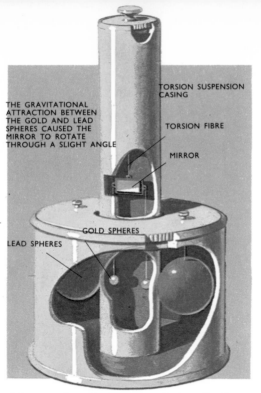

THE GRAVITATIONAL
ATTRACTION BETWEEN
THE GOLD AND LEAD
SPHERES CAUSED THE
MIRROR TO ROTATE
THROUGH A SLIGHT ANGLE

TORSION SUSPENSION
CASING

TORSION FIBRE

MIRROR

GOLD SPHERES

LEAD SPHERES

The torsion balance used by Professor Boys in 1930 to determine the constant of gravitation.

deflected until it is arrested by the torsional rigidity of the suspension ribbon. The *torsion balance* is another instrument which measures very tiny forces, such as those due to gravitation, magnetism, or electric charge.

Steel has a high resistance to torsion whereas string or thread has very little. When a body hung by a piece of steel wire is twisted to one side and then let go – it swings backwards and forwards. If the period (i.e. the time taken for a complete swing) is measured for different sizes of swing it is found to be independent of the size of swing. This means that even though the swings gradually die down due to air resistance and so on – the period remains the same. Such a device can therefore act as a timekeeper – and it is called a *torsional pendulum*. This type

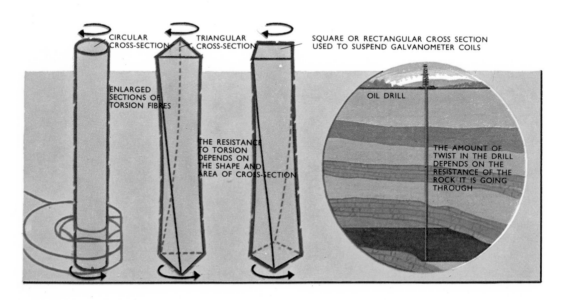

CIRCULAR
CROSS-SECTION

TRIANGULAR
CROSS-SECTION

SQUARE OR RECTANGULAR CROSS SECTION
USED TO SUSPEND GALVANOMETER COILS

ENLARGED
SECTIONS OF
TORSION FIBRES

THE RESISTANCE
TO TORSION
DEPENDS ON
THE SHAPE AND
AREA OF CROSS-SECTION

OIL DRILL

THE AMOUNT OF
TWIST IN THE DRILL
DEPENDS ON THE
RESISTANCE OF THE
ROCK IT IS GOING
THROUGH

Torsional Rigidity is defined to be the twist necessary to turn a known length of rod through a unit angle. Since the calculation of torsional rigidity is complicated, it is usually found experimentally with the torsion balance or the torsion pendulum.

of pendulum can be found in some modern clocks. The torsional rigidity of any specimen can be measured with the torsional pendulum as the period of the swing depends only on the torsional rigidity and the moment of inertia of the swinging body about the suspension. This period is independent of gravity.

In the torsion balance a light bar is hung at its middle from a fixed point by a fine wire or ribbon. Bodies whose gravitational or electrical attraction are going to be measured are attached to each end of the bar. When other large attracting masses or charged bodies are brought up close, the attraction between the small and large bodies pulls the bar around. It comes to rest with the suspension wire twisted. By reflecting a beam of light off a mirror attached to the wire the amount of twist is measured. The torsional rigidity of the suspension wire has previously been measured so that the attracting force is known. This instrument was used to measure the gravitational constant and to verify the inverse square law of electric charge.

CHAPTER SEVEN

How High will it Bounce?

MANY objects bounce when they are dropped on the floor, but none reaches the original height again. For instance, when an ivory ball is dropped on to a concrete floor from a height of 100 cm, it will rebound to a height of about 88 cm. A ball of lead dropped from the same height will not bounce as high. It will rise only 4 cm from the floor.

In any collision, whether it is between two moving particles or between one that is moving and another that is standing still, no *momentum* is lost. The momentum (mass times velocity) of one particle may be reduced by the collision, but the momentum of the other particle increases by a corresponding amount, so that the total momentum remains the same.

But actual collisions – between railway trucks, or between a tennis ball and the ground – are always accompanied by losses in kinetic energy. However, this energy is not lost altogether, it is converted into other forms of energy, mainly heat. A small amount of the kinetic energy is also converted into sound. Much more kinetic energy is converted in this way when lead collides with concrete.

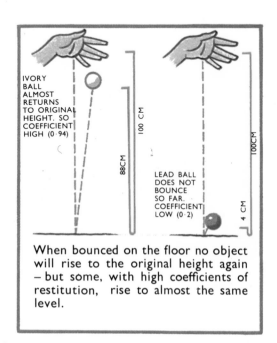

When bounced on the floor no object will rise to the original height again – but some, with high coefficients of restitution, rise to almost the same level.

144 CM

36 CM

9 CM

Energy is lost each time the ball strikes the ground. The height to which the ball will rise is always less than the height from which it was dropped.

ticles such as atoms and molecules of gases collide without loss of kinetic energy (i.e. are perfectly elastic). In fact the *kinetic theory of gases* is dependent on this assumption. If a collision is perfectly elastic the total kinetic energy of the particles before and after the collision is unchanged, although the energies of the individual particles will alter.

The most convenient way of finding the change in kinetic energy caused by a collision is to use an experimental law discovered by Sir Isaac Newton. For any pair of materials there is a constant – the *coefficient of restitution* – which is the ratio of the relative velocities of the two bodies after and before collision. The coefficient for a perfectly elastic collision, is 1, while that for an inelastic collision is 0. These are the extreme limits – the ball which returns to the height from which it was dropped (perfect bounce), and the ball which does not bounce at all (inelastic).

The coefficient of restitution for the pair of particles can be found experimentally, and once this constant is known, it is possible to calculate how two particles will collide without actually bringing them together. It is also possible to predict how high a ball will rise when it is bounced on the floor, or the velocity with which one billiard ball will travel after colliding with a second one.

If the particle does not rebound at all (it remains on the floor), the collision is *inelastic*. All the kinetic energy has been changed into other forms of energy. When a ball of putty is thrown at a concrete floor it flops out of shape – it does not bounce. Much of its kinetic energy is used up in overcoming the frictional forces between the molecules of the substances in the ball.

Collisions in which no kinetic energy is lost are *perfectly elastic*. When comparatively large objects collide the collisions are never perfect, but par-

Machines

CHAPTER EIGHT

Levers

LEVERS form one of the most important groups of simple machines, devices which enable energy to be used in the most advantageous way. At its simplest a lever is a rigid bar which can be turned freely round a fixed point (known as the fulcrum), and it is surprising what such a simple device can achieve. Given the right conditions a man could, for instance, lift an automobile on his own, a feat quite impossible without such a tool.

Three terms need to be explained in discussing levers. The resistance which is overcome is referred to as the *load*. The force used in moving it is called the *effort*—both of these may be measured in pounds weight. The *mechanical advantage* is the ratio of the resistance to the effort. Expressed as a formula:

$$\text{mechanical advantage} = \frac{\text{load}}{\text{effort}}$$

For example, if an effort of 100

Orders of Levers

The first order of levers has the fulcrum (pivot) in between the resistance at one end and the effort at the other. A simple example is the seesaw. Using this type of lever we can lift objects which normally we should find difficult if not impossible to move. As the diagram shows, the resistance and the effort move in opposite directions, one up, the other down. Now if the fulcrum of a lever is exactly halfway between effort and resistance the mechanical advantage will be one (i.e. a certain amount of effort is required to move an equal amount of resistance). If, on the other hand, the fulcrum is nearer to the resistance than it is to the effort there will be a greater mechanical advantage. From this it can been seen that a vital factor in the design of a lever is how far the resistance and the effort are from the fulcrum. The equation governing this factor is:

Resistance × Distance from Resistance to Fulcrum = Effort × Distance from Effort to Fulcrum

If the resistance is great, then the fulcrum must be nearer to it than to the effort. This equation applies to *all* kinds of levers.

If the resistance is tending to pull the lever in a clockwise direction, then the effort will be pulling it in an anti-clockwise direction. The two will be exerting opposing turning effects, or *moments*. (Moment equals the force applied multiplied by the perpendicular distance from the line of action of the force to the fulcrum.) For the two moments to balance each other the moment of the resistance must equal the moment of the effort. This is just another way of expressing the equation stated above. For the effort to actually move the resistance, a slightly greater effort will be required.

The second order of levers has the fulcrum at one end and the effort at the other, with the resistance in the middle. An everyday example is the wheel-barrow (complicated slightly by the addition of a wheel at the fulcrum). The load can be raised by lifting the handles of the barrow. Here again the mechanical advantage is greater the longer the distance between fulcrum and effort and the shorter the distance between fulcrum and load.

The third order of levers has the least mechanical advantage of all, and in fact a greater effort is needed than the amount of resistance moved. Here the fulcrum is at one end and the resistance at the other, with the effort in between. The human arm uses this type of leverage, with the elbow as the fulcrum, the resistance held in the hand and the effort applied by a contracting muscle in the upper arm attached to the forearm.

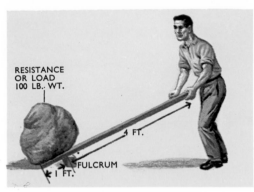

anti-clockwise moment = clockwise moment

$$1 \text{ ft.} \times 100 \text{ lbf.} = 4 \text{ ft.} \times \text{effort}$$
$$100 \text{ lbf.} = 4 \times \text{effort}$$
$$25 \text{ lbf.} = \text{effort}$$
$$\text{mechanical advantage} = \frac{\text{load}}{\text{effort}}$$
$$= \frac{100 \text{ lbf. wt.}}{25 \text{ lbf.}}$$
$$= 4$$

Using this lever, the effort needed is only a quarter of that needed to pick the stone off the ground.

lbf. has to be applied to a lever to raise a load (resistance) of 300 lbf., the mechanical advantage of that lever would be 3. The larger the mechanical advantage, the greater is the resistance that can be moved by the lever with the same effort. It must be emphasised, however, that neither levers nor any other kind of machine can create energy (indeed they tend to waste it for reasons which will be explained later) – they merely enable it to be used to better advantage.

For convenience levers are often divided into three *orders* or *classes*: the first, the second, and the third. In fact there is no actual difference in the principles by which they work, and similar calculations can be applied to all of them. The distinctions between them are concerned with the relative positions of the fulcrum, the effort and the resistance.

Levers do not create energy. How

then do they succeed in moving greater loads than is otherwise possible? The answer is quite simple. If they move a greater load they *do not move it so far* as they would if the effort was applied directly. Thus a man using a force of 100 lbf. to raise a resistance of 300 lbf. will raise it only one inch for every three inches he pushes on the lever. In the case of levers where there is a mechanical disadvantage (i.e. the effort has to be greater than the resistance) the resistance is moved *more* than the effort.

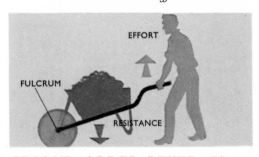

FIRST ORDER LEVER. The fulcrum is between resistance and effort.

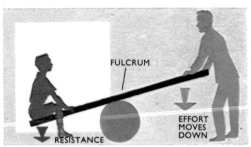

SECOND ORDER LEVER. The resistance is between fulcrum and effort.

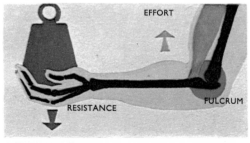

THIRD ORDER LEVER. The effort is between resistance and fulcrum.

25

CHAPTER NINE

Pulleys

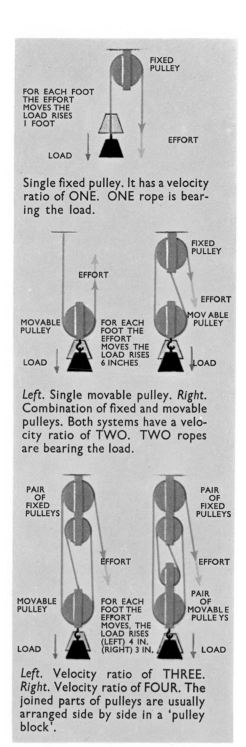

Single fixed pulley. It has a velocity ratio of ONE. ONE rope is bearing the load.

Left. Single movable pulley. *Right.* Combination of fixed and movable pulleys. Both systems have a velocity ratio of TWO. TWO ropes are bearing the load.

Left. Velocity ratio of THREE. *Right.* Velocity ratio of FOUR. The joined parts of pulleys are usually arranged side by side in a 'pulley block'.

PULLEYS can make it possible for a man to lift several times his own weight. The very action of bending down to lift an object from the floor is awkward and inconvenient and is certainly difficult if the object is heavy. It is very much easier to lift the object by heaving down on the rope of a pulley. There, the man's muscles are being put to their most efficient use and the standing position is certainly much more comfortable for him.

The simplest type of pulley block consists of a wheel, fixed from its centre to the ceiling in such a way that it is free to turn. Because it is fixed to the ceiling it is called a *fixed pulley*. A rope or chain runs over the wheel. The load to be lifted is attached to one end of the rope and the man hauls on the other end. The only advantage here is that of posture. The man can remain standing. But to raise a 50 lbf. load the effort he exerts must be at least 50 lbf. This machine has a *mechanical advantage* (M.A.) of one. The load (resistance) is the same as the effort. In practice, most pulley systems are designed to have a mechanical advantage of more than one so that much heavier loads can be raised.

If, with the aid of a pulley system, a force of 25 lbf. is able to raise a load of 50 lbf. then the pulley system has a mechanical advantage of two. If an effort of only 10 lbf. is able to raise a 50 lbf. load then the mechanical advantage is five.

$$\text{Mechanical advantage} = \frac{\text{load}}{\text{effort}}.$$

A single *movable* pulley can give a mechanical advantage of two. This time, one end of the *rope* is fixed and the pulley itself is cradled in the rope. The load is hung from the pulley block and the effort is used to pull upwards on the free end of the rope. Because the load is now hung from two ropes, each taking half of the strain, the effort needed is only half the size of the load. At first sight, this looks like a way of getting something for nothing, but in fact, it is not so. The *work* done *by* the effort is *never* less than the work done *on* the load. For every foot the rope is raised, the load rises only six inches. This is because both ropes have to be shortened.

With this movable pulley, the effort moves twice as far as the load moves. The pulley is said to have a *velocity ratio* (V.R.) of two.

$$\text{(V.R.)} = \frac{\text{distance moved by effort.}}{\text{distance moved by load.}}$$

If pulleys had no weight and there were no frictional forces opposing the raising of the load, then the mechanical advantage and velocity ratio would be equal. But in fact there are frictional forces acting and the pulley does weigh something and so extra effort is needed to overcome these factors. This in practice lessens the mechanical advantage, making it smaller than the velocity ratio.

Here, as a simplification, the pulleys are thought of as being weightless and frictionless.

Usually a pulley system consists of a combination of both fixed and movable pulley blocks, with the 'effort rope' arranged so that the man can haul down upon it.

CHAPTER TEN

Screws

THE screw is but one more class of simple machine, which, like levers, pulleys and inclined planes, is used for raising large loads by the application of quite small efforts. As with all these machines, the distance the large load is raised is small compared with the distance through which the effort moves.

A screw thread is a spiral cut made in the rod so that the screw may be regarded as a spiral inclined plane. For each complete turn of the screw it advances the same distance. This distance is the *pitch* of the screw, which can also be found by measuring along the length of the screw the distance between two adjacent ridges of the thread. The screw of a screw jack with a diameter of $\frac{3}{4}$ in. may have six threads to the inch, so the pitch of the thread is $\frac{1}{6}$ in. Thus for every one complete revolution of the tommy bar the lifting block moves $\frac{1}{6}$ in. up or down. If the tommy bar is a little over 6 in. in length it will trace out a circle of radius 6 in. for each complete revolution. The circumference of this circle is about 37·7 in., so that the load is raised $\frac{1}{6}$ in. for every 37.7 in. that the effort moves. Thus the velocity ratio of the screw jack

$$= \frac{e \text{ (effort distance)}}{l \text{ (load distance)}} = \frac{37 \cdot 7}{\frac{1}{6}} = 226.$$

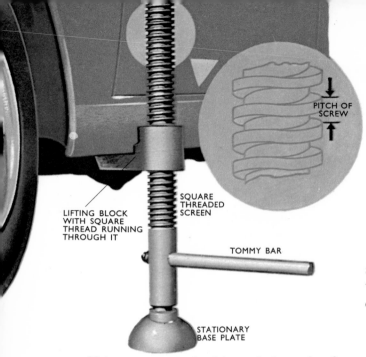

LIFTING BLOCK WITH SQUARE THREAD RUNNING THROUGH IT

SQUARE THREADED SCREEN

PITCH OF SCREW

TOMMY BAR

STATIONARY BASE PLATE

Using a screw jack with a velocity ratio of 226, one corner of the car can be raised by an effort of about $7\frac{1}{2}$ lbf.

Even if the thread of the screw is kept clean and is well greased, there is still likely to be considerable friction between the screw and both

the lifting block and the base plate. Thus a load 565 lbf. (about 5 cwt.f., which is the weight supported by one of the four wheels of a small car) could be lifted by a $2\frac{1}{2}$ lbf. effort if there were no friction. But in practice the effort would be between $7\frac{1}{2}$ lbf. and 10 lbf.

On account of the large frictional forces between the screw and the block, the load cannot 'unscrew' itself and run back under its own weight. This means that devices incorporating screws can be used not only for squeezing things in clamps, but also to keep them in a state of compression. Screw presses and clamps are used for this purpose in book binding and by carpenters when they are gluing joints. Likewise, objects can be held firmly in place in a bench vice by the clamping action of the screw thread it incorporates.

CHAPTER ELEVEN

Gears

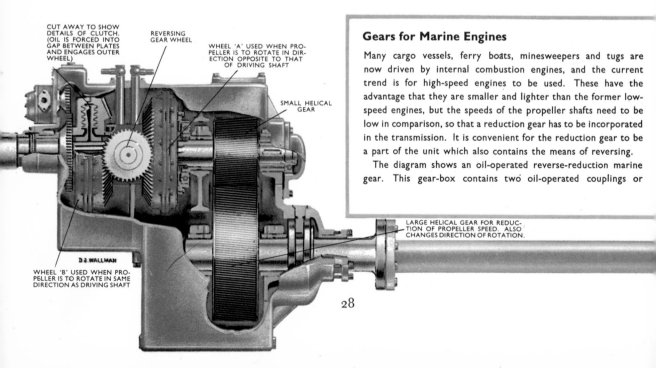

CUT AWAY TO SHOW DETAILS OF CLUTCH. (OIL IS FORCED INTO GAP BETWEEN PLATES AND ENGAGES OUTER WHEEL)

REVERSING GEAR WHEEL

WHEEL 'A' USED WHEN PRO-PELLER IS TO ROTATE IN DIR-ECTION OPPOSITE TO THAT OF DRIVING SHAFT

SMALL HELICAL GEAR

D.J.WALLMAN

WHEEL 'B' USED WHEN PRO-PELLER IS TO ROTATE IN SAME DIRECTION AS DRIVING SHAFT

LARGE HELICAL GEAR FOR REDUC-TION OF PROPELLER SPEED. ALSO CHANGES DIRECTION OF ROTATION.

Gears for Marine Engines

Many cargo vessels, ferry boats, minesweepers and tugs are now driven by internal combustion engines, and the current trend is for high-speed engines to be used. These have the advantage that they are smaller and lighter than the former low-speed engines, but the speeds of the propeller shafts need to be low in comparison, so that a reduction gear has to be incorporated in the transmission. It is convenient for the reduction gear to be a part of the unit which also contains the means of reversing.

The diagram shows an oil-operated reverse-reduction marine gear. This gear-box contains two oil-operated couplings or

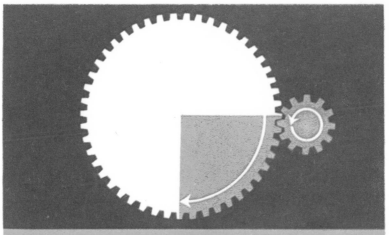

If the small gear (12 teeth) rotates once, the large gear (48 teeth) turns one quarter of a revolution. The velocity ratio of the system is 4.

THERE are certain circumstances in which the speed of a motor is not directly suitable for driving a particular machine. However, by means of a set of toothed wheels, or gears, it is possible to turn the machine at the speed for which it is designed. Such a system is particularly useful where a machine is driven by certain types of electric motor which have fixed speeds. Thus if the speed of the motor is 600 revolutions per minute, but the machine is only to turn 150 times in a minute, the gear wheel attached to the machine will have to turn at a quarter of the speed of that on the motor. This can be achieved if the motor gear wheel has 12 teeth while the one on the machine has 48 teeth, since one revolution of the small wheel, engages 12 teeth of the large wheel, turning it through $\frac{12}{48} = \frac{1}{4}$ of a revolution.

Since the velocity ratio of a machine may be defined as the velocity of the effort divided by the velocity of the load, the velocity ratio of the system

clutches, and by means of these either the forward or the reverse gear may be engaged. (The control system has been designed so that only one of the gears can be engaged at a time.) The shaft driven by the engine passes through both clutches. If this shaft is engaged with the clutch inside the wheel marked A, the small helical gear rotates in the same direction as the shaft. However, if the clutch inside the wheel marked B is engaged, the motion of this wheel is transmitted to wheel A by the small reversing gear wheel, so that wheel A and the helical gear rotate in the reverse direction. Reduction in the speed of rotation is achieved by the last pair of gear wheels.

of gears considered above is 4. This same figure is obtained by dividing the number of teeth on the machine (load) gear wheel (48) by the number on the motor (effort) wheel (12). The *gear ratio* is written as $12:48$ or $1:4$.

For this first example it has been assumed that the pair of gear wheels are in mesh, and by this means the rotational energy in one shaft is transmitted to the second shaft. However, it is not always convenient to

If there are 48 teeth on the chain-wheel and only 16 on the sprocket, one revolution of the chain-wheel results in the sprocket, and hence the rear wheel of the cycle, making three revolutions. From what has been said above, the velocity ratio of the gears on this machine is $\frac{16}{48}=\frac{1}{3}$.

A more realistic figure for the velocity ratio of the bicycle as a whole is obtained by considering the distance moved by the pedals in rela-

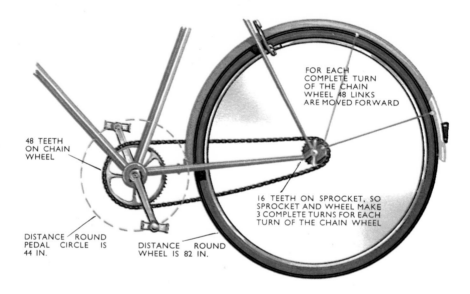

48 TEETH ON CHAIN WHEEL

FOR EACH COMPLETE TURN OF THE CHAIN WHEEL 48 LINKS ARE MOVED FORWARD

16 TEETH ON SPROCKET, SO SPROCKET AND WHEEL MAKE 3 COMPLETE TURNS FOR EACH TURN OF THE CHAIN WHEEL

DISTANCE ROUND PEDAL CIRCLE IS 44 IN.

DISTANCE ROUND WHEEL IS 82 IN.

In turning the chain-wheel once, the pedals move through 44 in., and as a result the wheel of the bicycle (circumference 82 in.) makes 3 revolutions. The velocity ratio is $44 \div (3 \times 82) = 0.18$.

have the two gears directly linked. An alternative is to have the two wheels linked by an endless belt or chain.

A chain system is used in bicycles. The rider does work by turning the pedals which causes the chain-wheel to rotate. By rotating the chain-wheel, the chain is put in tension, and the motion is transmitted to the rear wheel of the bicycle through another toothed wheel or sprocket.

tion to the distance the cycle moves forward. Assuming the cranks are 7 in. long and the wheels are 26 in. in diameter, the pedals will move about 44 in. for each turn of the chain-wheel, while the bicycle will move forward 3×82 in. (the circumference of a 26 in. wheel being 82 in.). The overall velocity ratio of the bicycle then be-

comes $\dfrac{44}{3 \times 82} = 0.18$.

Bodies in Motion

CHAPTER TWELVE

The Laws of Motion

THE FIRST LAW OF MOTION

'If a body is at rest
it will remain
at rest, and if it is in
motion it will
remain in motion at a
constant velocity
in a straight line, unless
it is acted upon
by an unbalanced
external force.'

When a bus moves away quickly from a stop the passengers are thrown backwards in their seats. If the driver brakes suddenly they are thrown forwards. Similarly the safety belts in a car are there to prevent passengers from being hurled against the windscreen if the car should be suddenly halted in a collision. There

When the car is brought to a sudden halt the driver tends to keep on moving as before. His forward movement throws him against the windscreen.

If the driver is wearing a safety belt he still experiences a tendency to keep on moving. But he does not hit the windscreen because the belt exerts a restraining force.

The car coasting downhill without friction tends to climb the next slope until it reaches a height equal to that from which it started. If the downhill slope is followed by a horizontal track (right), *the car must go on for ever trying to reach its original height.*

is obviously a tendency for anything moving or anything being carried along to keep on moving, if it can, and for objects at rest to remain at rest. This double tendency is called *inertia*. Sir Isaac Newton (1642–1727), one of the greatest scientists of all time, summarized the principle of inertia in his *first law of motion*. His version can be stated as follows: 'If a body is at rest it will remain at rest, and if it is in motion it will remain in motion at a constant velocity in a straight line, unless it is acted upon by an unbalanced external force'. Velocity means very much the same thing as speed, except that the movement is in one particular direction. Speed is a rate of movement which may be in varying directions.

The first law of motion is useful because it gives the real meaning of the word 'force'. We usually think of a force as the push or pull needed to move something. By twisting the law round, 'force' is defined more precisely as anything which alters the velocity of a body.

Newton's first law is based on the experiment of Galileo Galilei, an Italian scientist who made the first real study of motion. Galileo came to the conclusion that a body at rest tends to remain at rest, and a body moving in a straight line tends to continue with unchanging velocity for ever. We know, of course, that in ordinary circumstances a moving body cannot go on travelling for ever because of the slowing-down effects of friction and air resistance. Outside the Earth's atmosphere these forces are absent and it is then true that any moving object, whether it is a rocket or a speck of dust, will never be brought to rest, unless it is acted upon by the force of some heavenly body that it encounters on the way.

The Second Law of Motion

'If an unbalanced force acts on a body the acceleration
it produces is proportional to the size of the force and inversely proportional to the mass of the body.

Like the first law of motion, the second law is concerned with the way moving objects behave. Firstly it explains that the greater the force applied to an object the greater will be its rate of change of speed or 'acceleration'. This is clearly the case, for example, with a cyclist pushing the pedals round as he moves along. Assuming he is on a flat road, and that there is no wind, the harder he pushes the more quickly his speed will increase. (In theory it needs no effort at all to keep a steady speed.)

Acceleration is the increase of speed over a certain time. Thus a man push-

33

Acceleration is proportional to the force producing it. All the cyclists are of similar mass – the winner produces a faster increase in speed than his rivals during the final sprint because he exerts a greater force on his pedals.

ing hard on his pedals may increase his speed from 0 miles per hour to 5 m.p.h. in 5 seconds. His acceleration is said to be 1 mile per hour per second. A stronger man, pedalling with more effort, would accelerate faster (e.g. 2 miles per hour per second), though in each case the mass (which can be taken here to mean the same as weight) of the man and bicycle remain roughly the same.

The second part of the law states that the acceleration is inversely proportional to the mass. This simply means that the same force would accelerate a light object faster than a heavy one. For example a man can throw a cricket ball much farther and much faster than a cannon ball ten times its weight.

Combining the two parts of the law gives this: the force acting on a body is proportional to the mass of the body and to the acceleration it produces. The force is *equal* to the mass times the acceleration provided that the proper scientific units of force are employed.

The scientific units of force are the *poundal* (the force which will accelerate a mass of 1 lb. at 1 foot per second per second) and the Newton (the force needed to accelerate a mass of 1 kilogram at 1 meter per second per second). The units of force used in everyday life are the pound force and the kilogram force. 1 lb. force is equal to a force of 32 poundals and 1 gm. weight is equal to a force of 9.81 Newtons.

THE THIRD LAW OF MOTION

'To every action there is an equal and opposite reaction'

The third law of motion put forward by Isaac Newton considers the way forces act against each other. When you hold a matchbox on the palm of your hand, for example, the box presses down on the hand just as much as the hand presses up against the box. *Every time a force is exerted, in fact, it is balanced by a force exactly equal to it in the opposite direction.*

A simple way to show the working of this law is to fasten the hooks of two spring balances together. When

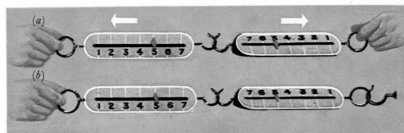

The spring balances record the equal and opposite forces (a) when both ends are pulled and (b) when only one end is pulled and the other fixed.

the ends of the balances are pulled apart, *both* of them register the same pull (e.g. 5 lbf.) and the springs are pulled out in opposite directions. Exactly the same effect occurs if one of the balances is fixed to the wall and the end of the other is pulled. Both will record equal and opposite forces.

Clear examples of equal and opposite forces are not hard to find. A spectacular one occurs in the rocket, where gases produced in the combustion-chamber push outwards with equal force in *all* directions. If the chamber were completely closed the rocket would not move. But as there is an opening at the rear, the gases cannot exert a force in that direction. Therefore the forces pushing on the *front* of the chamber are able to thrust the rocket forward.

A more homely example is the boat which slides away from the bank as the rower steps forward from it on to land. The backward thrust of the man's foot against the boat produces the equal and opposite force which enables him to land on the bank. That the foot does push backwards is shown by the fact that the boat moves away.

The escape of gases at the rear of the combustion-chamber enables the gases pushing against the forward end to lift the rocket.

The Equations

of Motion

Problems and calculations concerning moving objects involve such terms as distance travelled, time taken, constant acceleration, starting velocity and final velocity. Because the same terms are used over and over again it is very convenient to give them symbols. In fact it is necessary to use symbols here because without them it would be virtually impossible to construct formulae and *equations of motion*. Equations of motion give a simple method of finding, say, the final velocity of a moving object whose starting velocity, acceleration and distance travelled are known.

Time taken is given the symbol t. It is measured in seconds. Distance travelled is given the symbol s. It is measured in feet or centimetres. Final velocity is given the symbol v, starting velocity or initial velocity is given the symbol u. Velocities are measured in feet per second (ft./sec.) or centimetres per second (cm./sec.). Constant acceleration is given the symbol a. It is measured in feet per second per second (ft./sec./sec.) or centimetres per second per second (cm./sec./sec.). Although there are other units for measuring any of these quantities using them in calculations is liable to lead to mistakes.

The four equations of motion are:

$$v = u + at$$
$$\frac{u + v}{2} = \frac{s}{t}$$
$$s = ut + \tfrac{1}{2} at^2$$
$$v^2 = u^2 + 2as$$

Supposing a cyclist travelling at 8 ft./sec. accelerates at a rate of $1\frac{1}{2}$ ft./sec./sec. for 10 seconds. What speed does he attain? In this problem the final velocity (v) is to be found and the starting velocity (u), the acceleration (a) and the time taken (t) are known. Hence the equation to use is the first equation of motion, $v = u + at$, since it is the only one which does not include the unknown distance covered (s). The known values are $u = 8$ ft./sec., $a = 1\frac{1}{2}$ ft./sec./sec. $t = 10$ sec. and putting them into the equation gives:—

$v = 8 + 1\frac{1}{2} \times 10 = 8 + 15 = 23$ ft./sec.

So the cyclist attains a speed of 23 ft./sec. (about 15 m.p.h.). It is worth remembering that a speed of 60 m.p.h. is equal to 88 ft./sec.

The Derivation of the Equations of Motion

The first two equations are simply the definitions of acceleration and average velocity using symbols instead of words. Acceleration, a, is the increase in speed which takes place in one second. In t seconds the *increase* in speed is therefore at. The final velocity v after t seconds is the original (starting) velocity u plus the *increase* in velocity which took place during t seconds. Hence $v = u + at$, which is the first equation of motion.

Average speed is defined as distance travelled $\div$ time taken. Using symbols, the average speed $= \frac{s}{t}$. But if an object has a starting speed u and a final speed v the average of these two speeds is $\frac{u + v}{2}$. This is the average speed and is equal to $\frac{s}{t}$. Hence, $\frac{u + v}{2} = \frac{s}{t}$, the *second* equation of motion.

Unfortunately these two equations of motion do not cover every possible problem involving objects in motion. If, for example, the time, t, is unknown, neither equation can be used to .calculate, say, the final velocity, v. Similarly if the final velocity, v, is unknown it is impossible to calculate, say, the initial velocity u from either of these equations. For this reason two more equations of motion are needed, making four in all. The third and fourth equations are obtained by combining the first two.

The second equation can be written

$$\frac{s}{t} = \frac{u + v}{2}$$

multiply both sides by 2

$$\frac{2s}{t} = u + v$$

but $v = u + at$ from the first equation, so writing $u + at$ in place of v gives

$$\frac{2s}{t} = u + u + at = 2u + at$$

divide both sides by 2

$$\frac{s}{t} = u + \tfrac{1}{2} at$$

multiply both sides by t

$s = ut + \tfrac{1}{2} at \times t;$ or $s = ut + \tfrac{1}{2} at^2$

which is the *third* equation of motion.

To obtain the fourth equation each of the first two is arranged so that the symbol t alone appears on the left.

First equation $v = u + at$ is turned round to give $u + at = v$
subtract u from each side

$$at = v - u$$

divide by a

$$t = \frac{v - u}{a}.$$

Second equation $\frac{u + v}{2} = \frac{s}{t}$ is turned upside down to give

$$\frac{2}{u + v} = \frac{t}{s}$$

multiply both sides by s

$$\frac{2s}{u + v} = \frac{t}{s} \times s$$

So $t = \frac{2s}{u + v}$; but $t = \frac{v - u}{a}$,

so $\frac{v - u}{a} = \frac{2s}{u + v}$

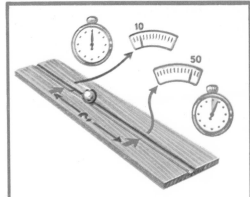

A ball bearing rolls down a sloping plank and by the time it reaches the first of two marks it has a speed of 10 cm./sec. By the time it reaches the second mark its speed has increased to 50 cm./sec. The ball is timed with a stop-watch as it rolls from the first to the second mark and is found to take 4 seconds. What is the distance between the marks? In this problem the distance travelled (s) is to be found while the starting velocity (u), the final velocity (v), and the time taken (t), are known. The best equation to use here is $\frac{u + v}{2} = \frac{s}{t}$, since this is the only one which does not include the unknown acceleration (a). The known values are $u = 10$ cm./sec., $v = 50$ cm./sec., $t = 4$ sec. Putting them into the equation $\frac{u + v}{2} = \frac{s}{t}$ gives $\frac{10 + 50}{2} = \frac{s}{4} = \frac{60}{2} = 30$. So if a quarter of the distance is 30 cm. the whole distance between the marks on the sloping planks is $4 \times 30 = 120$ cm.

To get rid of the fractions, multiply both sides by a

$$v - u = a \times \frac{2s}{u + v} = \frac{2as}{u + v}$$

multiply both sides by $(u + v)$

$$(u + v) \times (v - u) = (u + v) \times \frac{2as}{(u + v)}$$

$$u \times v - u \times u + v \times v - u \times v = 2as$$

$$v \times v - u \times u = 2as$$

$$v^2 - u^2 = 2as$$

adding u^2 to each side gives

$$v^2 = u^2 + 2as$$

which is the *fourth* equation.

$$v = u + at$$

$$\frac{u + v}{2} = \frac{s}{t}$$

$$s = ut + \tfrac{1}{2}at^2$$

$$v^2 = u^2 + 2as$$

t = time   s = distance travelled   a = acceleration

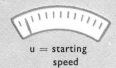

u = starting
speed

v = final
speed

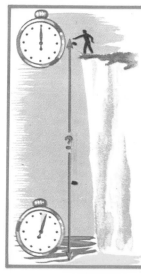

A stone dropped from the top of a cliff accelerates at a rate of 32 ft./sec./sec. as it falls. This is called the *acceleration due to gravity* and is given a symbol (*g*) of its own. If the stone falls for 3 seconds before it hits the ground, what is the height of the cliff? In this problem the distance travelled (*s*) is to be found and the acceleration (*a*) and the time taken (*t*) are known. The starting speed (*u*) is not given but it can be assumed that the stone started with no speed so *u* = 0. The equation to use here is $s = ut + \tfrac{1}{2}at^2$ since this is the only one which does not include the unknown final velocity (*v*). The known values are *u* = 0, *t* = 3 sec., *a* = 32 ft./sec./sec. and putting them into the equation gives:—

$s = 0 \times 3 + \tfrac{1}{2} \times 32 \times 3 \times 3 = 0 + 144 = 144$ feet.

(The result of multiplying any number by zero is always zero, hence $0 \times 3 = 0$.) So the cliff is 144 feet high.

A lift moving with a speed of 20 ft./sec. slows down until, after it has travelled 16 feet, its speed is only 12 ft./sec. What is the acceleration? The initial velocity (*u*), the final velocity (*v*) and the distance travelled (*s*) are known, and the acceleration (*a*) is to be found. The best equation to use here is $v^2 = u^2 + 2as$ since this is the one which does not include the unknown time (*t*). Putting the known values *u* = 20 ft./sec., *v* = 12 ft./sec., *s* = 16 feet, into the equation gives:—

$$12 \times 12 = 20 \times 20 + 2 \times a \times 16$$
$$144 = 400 \quad + \quad 32 \times a$$

Taking 400 away from each side of the equation gives:—

$$(144 - 400) = (400 - 400) + 32 \times a$$
$$-256 = 32 \times a$$

so that $32 \times a = minus\ 256$. Dividing both sides of the equation by 32 gives:—

$$a = minus\ \frac{256}{32} = minus\ 8.$$

So the acceleration of the lift is *minus* 8 ft./sec./sec. The *minus* sign means the object is not speeding up but is slowing down. In other words, the lift has a *retardation* (the opposite of acceleration) of 8 ft./sec./sec.

CHAPTER THIRTEEN

Fletcher's Trolley Experiment

IF a force acts on a body, the *acceleration* it produces on that body is proportional to the size of the *force* and is inversely proportional to the *mass* of the body. Newton stated this in the second of his three laws of motion. The law can be proved quite simply by using a piece of apparatus called Fletcher's Trolley.

A wheeled trolley runs on a smooth board and carries a strip of paper on the top. The trolley is the *mass* that is *accelerated*. At the end of the board is a pulley and a scale-pan. Weights on the scale pan provide the *force* that accelerates the trolley. Attached to the board is a vibrating metal strip with an inked brush at the end. As the trolley runs under the brush it receives a wavy trace of the vibrations. This trace

is used to measure the acceleration.

When the weights pull the trolley along, they have first to overcome the friction acting in the wheels and between the wheels and the board. The friction must be balanced before the experiment is started. This is done by tilting the board slightly until the trolley just runs down the board at a steady speed. The added weights will then be employed solely in accelerating the trolley.

The time for one vibration (period) of the metal strip can be found by timing a large number of vibrations. The experiment can then be carried out. A suitable weight—say ten grams—is put on the pan and the brush set vibrating. The trolley is then released. It picks up a trace from the brush and,

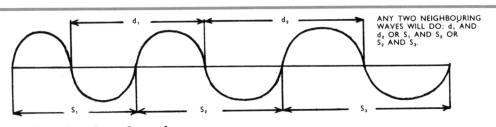

ANY TWO NEIGHBOURING WAVES WILL DO: d_1 AND d_2 OR S_1 AND S_2 OR S_2 AND S_3.

Finding the Acceleration

Take any two neighbouring waves of the trace. The time for each is t seconds (found from the rate of vibration of the brush) and their lengths in centimetres are d_1 and d_2.

Average speed is distance divided by time. The average speeds are then $\dfrac{d_1}{t}$ cm/sec and $\dfrac{d_2}{t}$ cm/sec. The average speed will be the speed at the mid-point of each trace. The time between two consecutive mid-points is equal to one time interval (i.e., t seconds) In t seconds the speed increases by $\dfrac{d_2}{t} - \dfrac{d_1}{t} = \dfrac{d_2 - d_1}{t}$ cm/sec. Therefore the gain in speed in one second (i.e. the acceleration) is $\dfrac{d_2 - d_1}{t} \times \dfrac{1}{t}$. The acceleration is therefore $\dfrac{d_2 - d_1}{t^2}$.

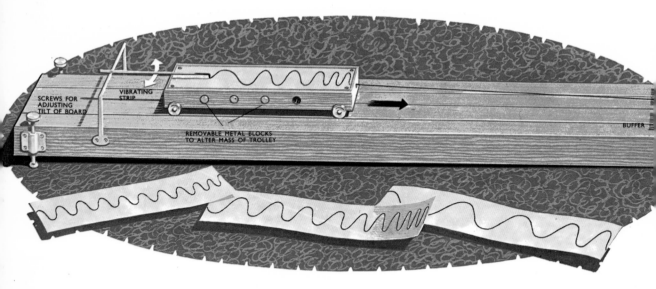

As it runs under the vibrating brush, the trolley collects a trace from which the acceleration can be calculated. The shape of the trace depends upon the weight on the scale pan. An alternative arrangement is to have the brush mounted on the trolley. The trace is then inked on to paper on the board. A longer trace is obtained but the result is the same.

because the trolley gets faster and faster, the trace 'opens out'. The time for each wave is the same but their lengths increase. The time and distance are known and so the average speed can be worked out for each part of the trace. As the average speed is known for each part, the acceleration can be worked out. If the experiment is carried out with several different weights on the scale pan, several values for the acceleration are obtained. This is done by removing metal blocks from the trolley and placing them in the scale pan. This changes the accelerating force but keeps the mass of the system constant. Before each accelerating force is added the friction is balanced as before. The

value for acceleration divided by the force (i.e., the weight on the pan) should be constant. In other words, *the acceleration is proportional to the force producing it.*

The second part of the law says that the acceleration is inversely proportional to the mass when the accelerating force is constant. It can be proved by having a fixed weight on the pan and changing the mass of the trolley by removing one or more metal blocks. The results show that the larger the mass of the trolley the smaller the acceleration. Acceleration is proportional to $\frac{1}{mass}$, or mass times acceleration is constant.

CHAPTER FOURTEEN

Centrifugal Force

AN object which moves round in a circle is continually accelerating. In other words its velocity is continually changing (see Newton's Laws of Motion on pages 32 and 33). This may seem very strange unless you remember that velocity is speed in a given direction. A change of velocity can thus be caused if *either* the speed changes *or* the direction changes. An object moving round in a circle is thus always accelerating because its direction of motion is always changing. A force must be exerted for an acceleration to take place, and the force which makes an object move round in a circle is known as *centripetal force*. Newton's Third Law (page 34) gives us the connection between this and the more familiar *centrifugal force*.

If you whirl a bucket round at arm's length the centripetal force is the inward action of the arm on the bucket. The centrifugal force is the outward reaction of the bucket on the arm. As soon as the action ceases so does the reaction. The driver of an accelerating car can feel the push of the seat in his back. The reaction to this is the push of his body backwards on the seat. When the car stops accelerating its push on the driver ceases and so does the reaction of the driver on the seat and he carries on moving with a constant velocity. If you released the bucket it would move off with a constant velocity *in the direction it was moving at the instant you released it*. This direction is a tangent to the circle. If there is water in the bucket while it is being whirled round, the reaction of the water against the side of the bucket (the centrifugal force) keeps the water in the bucket.

The acceleration caused by moving in a circle increases if the speed round the circle increases and also if the radius gets smaller. The inward centripetal force needed to make a train go round a curve may be provided by the push of the track on the wheels. This push can be increased by banking the track and the train can thus travel faster or in a smaller curve. A more dramatic example is the Wall of Death rider. The faster he goes the farther up the wall he must rise in

The centrifugal force holds the water in the bucket.

The centrifuge is used for separating solid from liquid or for separating a mixture of two liquids of different density.

order to get a big enough push to cause the increased acceleration.

If the speed was too great the centripetal force would not be large enough to cause the necessary acceleration and the object would try to move out to a larger circle to reduce the acceleration. In the case of the train this would mean it would topple over towards the outside of the curve. This principle is used in a centrifuge to separate substances of different densities, particularly suspensions of solids in liquids and also mixtures of liquids. The more dense a substance is the more force is needed to keep it moving in a circle. If this force is not applied it will try to move out to a larger radius. In this way milk can be separated very quickly from the less dense cream.

CHAPTER FIFTEEN

Relative Velocity

TWO trains are standing beside one another in a station and one starts to move. A passenger in one train thinks it is his train that is moving. Certainly he seems to be moving past the windows and doors of the carriages of the other train. Suddenly he turns to look through the opposite window and, to his disappointment, he finds that his window is still opposite the door of the refreshment room on the station platform. His train is still standing in the station so it must have been the train standing at the next platform which has departed in the *opposite direction*.

Many railway passengers must have experienced this rather strange sensation at one time or another. Although at first the passenger thinks his

train is moving, he can only be really certain that one train is moving in relation to the other. But a porter standing on the platform knows which train is moving because he is *stationary* and can tell when other objects are moving.

For velocity to have any meaning at all it must be measured in relation to some reference point. This reference may be stationary or may itself be moving. For instance, an express train appears to be moving much faster to someone standing beside the track than to a passenger in a slow moving train travelling in the same direction alongside the express.

The stationary observer and the moving passenger get different results when they measure the velocity of the express train because of the difference in their own velocities. If no reference is mentioned, it is normal to assume that all velocities are measured with reference to the stationary ground. Velocities measured from a moving observation point are called *relative velocities*, but, to avoid confusion in problems concerning moving objects, the velocity of the observer or the position of the observation point should always be stated.

Perhaps a stationary bystander sees an express train travelling North at a velocity of 60 m.p.h. and a slow train travelling alongside in the same direction at 35 m.p.h. (These are the velocities of each train relative to the ground). But to someone in the slow train, the express appears to be moving North at only 25 m.p.h. The velocity of the express relative to the slow one is 25 m.p.h. in a Northerly direction.

The two trains are moving along parallel paths, and it is an easy matter to calculate the velocity of one relative to the other, provided their velocities relative to the ground are already known. For instance the velocity of the express train relative to the slow train was found by *subtracting* their respective velocities (60 − 35 = 25 m.p.h.). The velocity of the slow train relative to the express is 35 − 60 = −25 m.p.h. The minus sign here indicates that to someone in the express the slow train appears to be going backwards. It has a relative velocity of 25 m.p.h. in a Southerly direction.

If instead, the two trains were moving in opposite directions (the slow train going South and the express, North) the velocity of one relative to the other is found by adding together the *speeds* of each relative to the ground. (This is the same as subtracting their velocities, because they are

heading in different directions. The velocity of one will be negative and subtracting a negative number is the same as adding a positive number).

To someone on the slow train heading South, the express seems to be rushing Northwards, at 95 m.p.h. (60 + 35). The passengers in the ex-

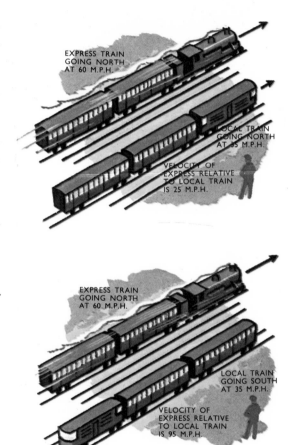

When both trains are going in the same direction (North), the velocity of the express travelling at 60 m.p.h. relative to the slow train (35 m.p.h.) is 25 m.p.h. in a Northerly direction. However, if the slow train were going South, the relative velocity of the express is 95 m.p.h.

POSITION OF
TARGET WHEN
GUN IS FIRED

LINE OF FIRE
FOR SHOT TO
STRIKE MOVING
TARGET

To hit the moving 'clay pigeon' the gun has to be aimed at a point in front of it. This is another instance of relative velocities.

press think the same thing about the slow train, only to them it appears to be speeding Southwards.

These trains have been running on parallel tracks and the relative velocity problems concerning them are quite simple. But a ship has no such lines to guide its path and can be steered in any direction. Consequently, the problems connected with the relative velocities of ships are more complicated.

If the ship is moving forward at 15 knots (a knot is a speed of one nautical mile per hour), and a passenger is sitting in a deck chair (i.e. he is stationary relative to the ship) he, too, will be moving forward at 15 knots relative to an observer on a nearby jetty. (It is assumed that the effects of winds and currents may be neglected).

If the man now gets up and walks forward with a velocity of 3 knots, the observer sees him moving at 18 knots – the passenger's velocity relative to the ship (3 knots) plus the ship's velocity relative to the observer (15 knots). But if, instead, the passenger walked across from the port (left) side to the starboard (right) side of the deck at 3 knots, the observer on the jetty would see him taking a diagonal path. While the passenger on the deck was

44

PASSENGER HAS SAME VELOCITY AS SHIP

3 KNOTS

15 KNOTS

VELOCITY OF PASSENGER RELATIVE TO JETTY IS 15 + 3 = 18 KNOTS

While the passenger remains seated his velocity is the same as the ship's (15 knots), but when he moves forward his velocity relative to the jetty is greater (18 knots). If he walks across the deck, he follows a diagonal path as viewed from the jetty. His velocity relative to the jetty can be found from the 'triangle of velocities'.

MAN WALKS ACROSS DECK AT 3 KNOTS

VELY. OF SHIP – 15 KNOTS

VELY. OF MAN RELATIVE TO JETTY – 15·2 KNOTS

VELY. OF MAN 3 KNOTS

AS SEEN FROM THE JETTY THE MAN APPEARS TO HAVE MOVED DIAGONALLY

crossing the deck at 3 knots relative to the ship, the ship was carrying him forward at 15 knots relative to the observer on the jetty.

The actual velocity of the passenger relative to the observer on the jetty may be found by drawing a *triangle of velocities*. One side of the triangle is drawn to represent in size and direc-

tion the velocity of the ship relative to the jetty – the line is drawn 15 units long to represent the speed of 15 knots. This shows where the passenger would have been, had he not walked across the deck (i.e. had remained in one place on the deck). From the end of this line another line is drawn at right-angles to represent in size and direc-

45

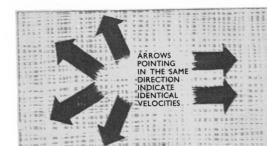

ARROWS
POINTING
IN THE SAME
DIRECTION
INDICATE
IDENTICAL
VELOCITIES

Speed is the rate of change of position of an object with time, while velocity is the rate of change of position in a particular direction. These arrows represent a group of objects moving at the same speed, but only two have the same velocity.

tion the velocity of the man. This second line is only 3 units long to represent the passenger's velocity of 3 knots relative to the ship. The triangle is then completed by drawing in the third side. This line represents in size and direction the velocity of the passenger relative to the observer on the jetty. The size of the velocity can be found by measuring the length of the line.

Cross winds and currents can send a ship miles off course if no allowance is made for them. However, by similar reasoning to the above the effects of wind or current on the course of a ship can be found and in setting course allowance is made for them. If this is done correctly the ship should arrive safely in port.

Energy

CHAPTER SIXTEEN

Work, Energy and Power

THERE are many ways of moving both objects and ourselves. Every time something is moved *work* is being done. Animals have been trained to pull things. Man has used the wind (windmills and sails) and flowing water to do much work for him. These forces cannot always be depended upon —the wind might drop and a drought may occur—so engines of many kinds have been devised for moving things, so making our tasks easier. Whenever an object is moved *work* is being done. In the science of Physics, work means moving a force through a distance.

If something has to be moved it is pushed, pulled or lifted and *work* is being done. *Energy* is the ability to move things or *ability to do work*. Our *energy* for *work* comes from the food we eat. Consider the work done by a builder. The amount of work we do can be accurately measured after studying some Physics. Before doing our calculations several questions have to be asked.

First, how heavy are the stone blocks and bricks? Secondly, how far (or high) must they be moved? Weights are measured in pounds force (lbf.) and distances are measured in feet (ft.). Both weight and distance have to be taken into account if you wish to know exactly how much work you are going to do. It might take just as much work to lift a small brick a long distance as it would to move a large stone block a shorter distance.

It is easy to calculate the work done in our tasks. If a brick weighs $7\frac{1}{2}$ lbf. and you lift it up a ladder to a height 20 ft. above the ground, you do 150 ft. lbf. of work:

Work = Weight × distance moved
= $7\frac{1}{2}$ × 20 ft. lbf.
= 150 ft. lbf.

The same amount of work would be involved if a stone block weighing 50 lb. was lifted 3 feet.

If you merely held a stone or brick without moving it, a physicist would say that you were not doing work.

Another question may be asked. How fast is the work to be done? Are you a fast or a slow worker? It would not make any difference to the total work done if you slowly climbed a ladder with your stone or whether you ran up it. The *work done* is the same when a given weight is moved a certain distance whether the movement is slow or quick. However, the *power* is different as the *rate of doing work* is different. *Power* is the work done in a second. Thus if you climbed a 20-ft. ladder with a 3 lbf. stone in 10 seconds, you are doing 60 ft. lbf. of work in 10 seconds or 6 ft. lbf. of work in 1 second. Power = 6 ft. lbf. per sec.

	H.P.	Foot lbf. per sec.	Foot lbf. per min.
Weightlifter	$\frac{1}{10}$	55	3,300
Horse	1	550	33,000
Motor-car	10	5,500	330,000
Diesel	1,000	550,000	33,000,000

Power=work done per second
If you ran up the same ladder with
the same stone in 3 seconds, work is
the same, but the power is now 20 ft.
lbf. per second.

A good horse was found to do 550
ft. lbf. in 1 second, and power is often
given in horsepower.

550 ft. lbf. per second = 1 Horsepower (h.p.).

In the MKS system of units, the
unit of work is the *joule*. The unit of
power is the *watt*, which is the rate of
working of one joule per second.

1 Horsepower = 746 watts.

Energy

The ability to move things is just
one form of energy – mechanical
energy. Other forms include heat

*The Beagle-Wallis lightweight autogyro
has a 65 h.p. engine, and cruises at 75
m.p.h. The rate of climb is 1,250 ft./min.
If the take-off weight was 500 lbf., the
work done in a minute would be 500 ×
1,250 = 625,000 ft. lbf.*

energy, electrical energy, chemical
energy, magnetic energy and atomic
energy. Not only is energy found in
various different forms, one form can
quite easily (though with a certain
amount of wastage) be converted into
another. In a power station, for example, heat energy (used to produce
the steam) is converted into mechanical energy (in a turbine) which
drives the generator which in turn
produces electrical energy which can
be used to produce light energy and
heat energy in a lamp.

Surprisingly enough we can never
destroy energy. When we move a
finger we are using up energy, and,
more often than not, have no useful
work to show for it. But energy has
not been destroyed—only converted
into some other form. In this case it
may have been given as heat to the
air surrounding the finger. It may
be *wasted*, but never *lost*. Careful
measurements have shown that
energy is never created nor destroyed.
This is known as the *Law of Conserva-*

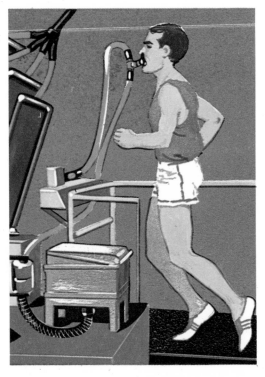

*Chemical energy is locked up in the food
we eat: when the food combines with
oxygen this energy is released. This
athlete is measuring the amount of oxygen
he uses during exercise.*

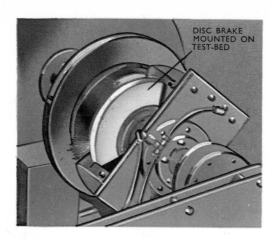

One of the disc brakes from a racing car. The kinetic energy *possessed by the moving wheel is not destroyed when the brake is applied – it is converted into* heat energy. *On test the disc is nearly white-hot.*

The wound-up spring of a clock or watch possesses potential (*stored*) *energy. This is released slowly* (*with the aid of an escapement mechanism*) *and reappears as the* kinetic energy *of the moving hands.*

tion of Energy. It means, in fact, that the total amount of energy in the whole universe has always been the same, and will always be the same.

Under certain circumstances, matter can be converted into energy. In an atomic explosion, for example, a minute quantity of matter is converted into a vast amount of energy. This is not a contradiction of the Law of Conservation of Energy, since energy is not being created from *nothing*, but from *matter*. Matter is just another form of energy.

Virtually the whole of physics is concerned in some way with the study of energy. Mechanical energy is considered to be either *kinetic* (associated with *moving* objects) or *potential* which is stored up ready to be used. The water rushing down a waterfall has *kinetic* energy. (In fact this energy is available for doing useful work such as driving a turbine). But since energy is never created (nor destroyed) the water must have had some kind of energy before it started to fall. The

energy which the water at the top of the waterfall possesses because of its position is an example of *potential* energy. The kinetic energy of the moving water at the foot of the waterfall is less than its potential energy at the top. Energy has been wasted in friction between water molecules and appears as heat, so the water at the bottom should be slightly warmer than that at the top.

The potential energy of the water before it starts to fall is equal to the work which would have to be performed in raising the water, bucket by bucket, from the bottom of the waterfall to the top. This can be calculated easily enough.

The kinetic energy of the water in motion is governed by its velocity (speed) and its mass. It is calculated from the formula *kinetic energy* $= \frac{1}{2} m v^2$ where m is the mass and v is the velocity (v^2 is the square of the velocity, *i.e.* the velocity multiplied by itself). If the mass is in pounds and the velocity is in feet per second then the formula gives the kinetic energy in *foot-poundals*. If the mass is in kilograms and the velocity is in metres per second the formula gives the kinetic energy in joules.

All the different forms of energy (heat, electrical, light, etc.) could be measured in joules. In practice each kind of energy tends to have its own units although Electrical Energy and Mechanical Energy in the Metric system are measured in joules. Heat Energy is measured in calories but may also be measured in joules (1 calorie = 4.18 joules).

CHAPTER SEVENTEEN

Inertia and Moments of Inertia

IT would be very surprising if a stationary ball started to move of its own accord. If the ball is at rest, then its natural tendency is to stay at rest. Every material thing has the same tendency (called *inertia*) to stay in exactly the same state. The only way of shifting it is by applying a force.

When the ball is moving steadily, its inertia tends to keep it moving. The bigger the mass of the ball (the amount of matter in it) the more inertia it has. It needs a more powerful shove to move it (to overcome its inertia), and a bigger force acting in the opposite direction to slow it down. Inertia depends on the mass of a body.

Anyone who has whirled a ball round on the end of a string knows that the exertion required to get it moving is more than the force necessary to push it so that it moves in a straight line. Once the ball is moving, it is more difficult to slow it down again. Its inertia has been increased considerably without adding to its mass (the string contributes practically no mass at all). So inertia depends on other factors besides the mass of the ball. It depends on the shape and size of the whole whirling object, i.e. string

Particles spinning near the axis of rotation have less inertia than those spinning a long way from the axis.

plus ball on the end of it. As the length of the string increases, the inertia increases. The ball exerts a force some distance away from the hand holding the string. A force multiplied by its distance from the turning point is called a *moment*. In the same way, the ball has a *moment of inertia* about its turning point. The moment of inertia takes into account the mass of the ball, and its distance from the turning point. It is a measure of the force needed to change the whirling movement in any way. Another useful property of the *moment of inertia* is that it shows how much *energy* the whirling ball possesses.

A ball at the end of a long piece of string moves faster through the air than a ball at the end of the short piece of string, if they both complete just as many rotations per second. The ball moves faster, so it has more energy. The ball is further away from the turning point, so it has a bigger *moment of inertia*.

Flywheels and Inertia

The conventional car engine does not produce driving energy continuously. As the pistons move up and down in the cylinders, energy is released in jerky bursts. Without the flywheel, the bursts of energy would be transmitted, through the crankshaft (to which the pistons are connected) to the wheels. The car would not run smoothly.

The car flywheel, however, is built

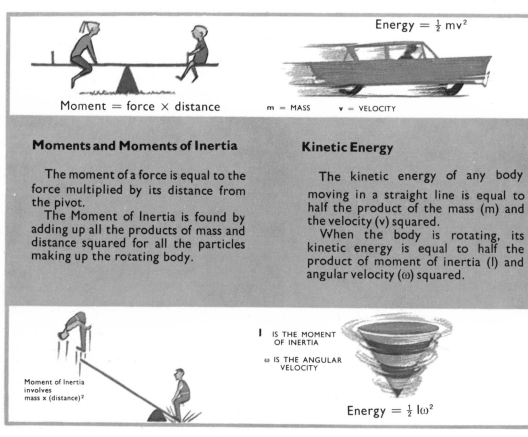

Energy = $\frac{1}{2} mv^2$

Moment = force × distance

m = MASS   v = VELOCITY

Moments and Moments of Inertia

The moment of a force is equal to the force multiplied by its distance from the pivot.

The Moment of Inertia is found by adding up all the products of mass and distance squared for all the particles making up the rotating body.

Kinetic Energy

The kinetic energy of any body moving in a straight line is equal to half the product of the mass (m) and the velocity (v) squared.

When the body is rotating, its kinetic energy is equal to half the product of moment of inertia (I) and angular velocity (ω) squared.

Moment of Inertia involves mass x (distance)²

I IS THE MOMENT OF INERTIA

ω IS THE ANGULAR VELOCITY

Energy = $\frac{1}{2} I\omega^2$

The moment of inertia of the flywheel can be calculated by working out the contribution of every piece of the flywheel.

A bigger moment of inertia (for the same mass) comes when the mass is concentrated in the rim. It is farthest from the axis.

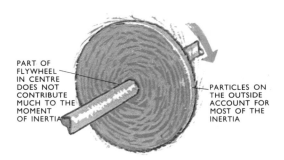

PART OF
FLYWHEEL
IN CENTRE
DOES NOT
CONTRIBUTE
MUCH TO THE
MOMENT
OF INERTIA

PARTICLES ON
THE OUTSIDE
ACCOUNT FOR
MOST OF THE
INERTIA

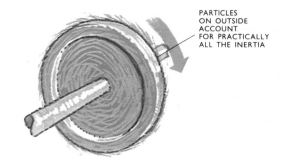

PARTICLES
ON OUTSIDE
ACCOUNT
FOR PRACTICALLY
ALL THE INERTIA

The inertia of the car's flywheel smoothes out the jerky movement of the pistons. The flywheel is attached to the crankshaft.

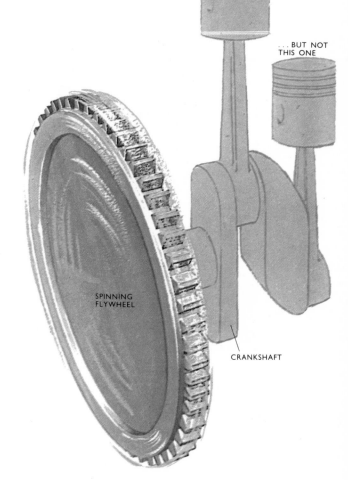

EXPLOSION IN
CYLINDER PUSHES
THIS PISTON . . .

. . . BUT NOT
THIS ONE

SPINNING
FLYWHEEL

CRANKSHAFT

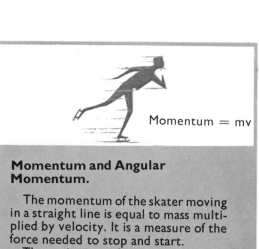

Momentum = mv

Momentum and Angular Momentum.

The momentum of the skater moving in a straight line is equal to mass multiplied by velocity. It is a measure of the force needed to stop and start.

The spinning skater has angular momentum, a measure of the turning force needed to start and stop the spin. It is equal to Moment of Inertia multiplied by angular velocity.

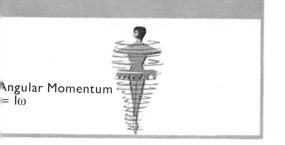

Angular Momentum
= Iω

to have *inertia*. It is a thick-rimmed steel disc attached to the end of the crankshaft. Once it is set rotating, its inertia tends to keep it rotating. The flywheel resists changes in its rotation, so it smoothes out the jerkiness in the piston movement. Inertia keeps the crankshaft and the wheels turning smoothly.

The thicker rim of the flywheel gives it a moment of inertia bigger than if the same amount of metal (i.e. the same mass) were cast into a uniformly flat disc. The mass of the flywheel is concentrated as far from the turning-point as possible. This leads to a bigger *moment of inertia*.

CHAPTER EIGHTEEN

Momentum

WHEN a bull is chasing a boy velocities are all important. However, if only the velocities are known, it is impossible to work out what will happen if boy and bull collide. Then their masses, as well as their velocities, will be important. One of the most useful quantities to know is the *momentum*, or the product of mass and velocity (i.e. momentum is mass × velocity). For the momentum is the *quantity of motion*. The bull, with its large mass, has obviously more momentum than the boy, although both have the same velocity. The momentum of a body gives an indication of the effort (or, more exactly, the *impulse*) needed to get the body moving or, for that matter, to stop it. A lot of effort has been needed to get the bull moving at 12 miles per hour. But not so much effort has been required for the boy to be moving at the same velocity.

In the same way, the boy can be stopped relatively easily. A small impulse applied in the opposite direction would slow him down – in other words reduce his momentum. The same impulse would cause the same change of momentum of the bull, but would cause a much smaller change in the bull's velocity.

So the momentum is important when the motion is being changed in any way – in particular it is important in sudden collisions, such as the bouncing of a ball against the ground, the impact between tennis racquet and

Both boy and bull are moving with the same velocity. But since the bull has a greater mass than the boy, it has more momentum.

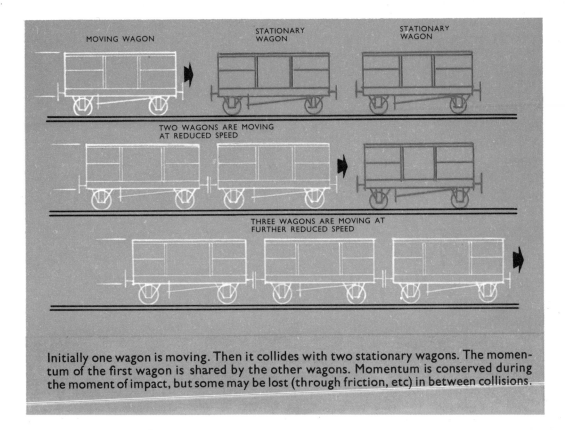

Initially one wagon is moving. Then it collides with two stationary wagons. The momentum of the first wagon is shared by the other wagons. Momentum is conserved during the moment of impact, but some may be lost (through friction, etc) in between collisions.

ball, or the head-on collision between two cars.

Momentum is conserved

One of the reasons for calculating momentum is that, in sudden collisions or in explosions, it is *conserved*. The momentum before the collision or explosion is exactly the same as the momentum afterwards. This is particularly useful, because the velocities of the objects, before and afterwards, can be worked out.

In one of the examples shown here, a railway wagon is given an impulse so

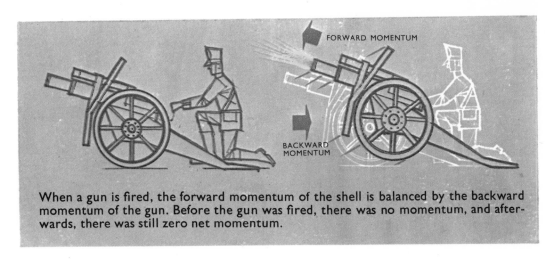

When a gun is fired, the forward momentum of the shell is balanced by the backward momentum of the gun. Before the gun was fired, there was no momentum, and afterwards, there was still zero net momentum.

that it moves towards a stationary wagon. The two collide, join together, and then start to move together. Because momentum is conserved, the momentum of the two wagons before their collision is equal to their combined momentum after the collision. The stationary wagon had initially no momentum – it had no velocity. The moving wagon had a momentum equal to its mass times its velocity. It carried all the momentum involved in the collision.

Afterwards two wagons are moving. Twice the amount of mass is in motion, but, so that the momentum is unchanged, their velocity must be *half* the velocity of the single wagon.

Sometimes momentum seems to have appeared from nowhere. This is so when a gun is fired. As a result of the explosion within the barrel, a bullet is given a forward impulse (and therefore momentum). The gun was stationary just before the firing, so it had no momentum.

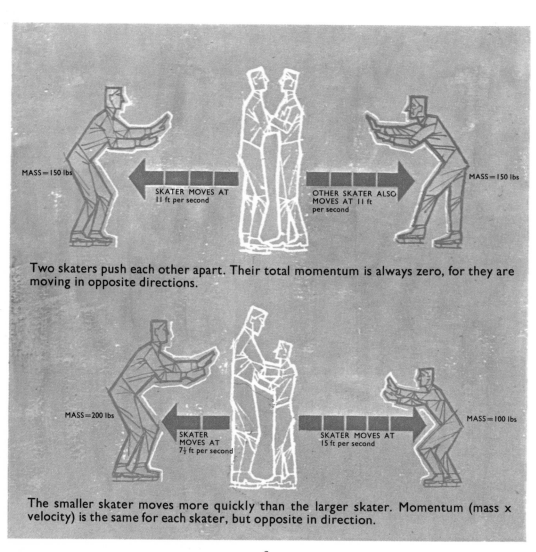

MASS = 150 lbs

SKATER MOVES AT 11 ft per second

OTHER SKATER ALSO MOVES AT 11 ft per second

MASS = 150 lbs

Two skaters push each other apart. Their total momentum is always zero, for they are moving in opposite directions.

MASS = 200 lbs

SKATER MOVES AT 7½ ft per second

SKATER MOVES AT 15 ft per second

MASS = 100 lbs

The smaller skater moves more quickly than the larger skater. Momentum (mass × velocity) is the same for each skater, but opposite in direction.

However, momentum is conserved, for the gun always *recoils*. It moves backwards and its momentum is equal to the forward momentum of the bullet, but of course it is in the *opposite direction*. The bullet has a 'positive' momentum, and the gun a 'negative' momentum. When the total momentum of both gun and bullet is added up, the 'positive' momentum cancels out the 'negative' momentum, so there is *no resultant momentum*. Momentum has been conserved, for there was also none before the explosion.

If two skaters push each other apart, they travel in opposite directions. This is a similar sort of situation to the bullet and gun, only the relationships between the velocities and masses of each of the moving things can be seen more clearly. Initially the skaters have no momentum, since they are standing still. Just after they have pushed away from each other, their *total* momentum is still zero, for they are travelling in opposite directions. A 'positive' momentum in one direction is exactly cancelled out by a 'negative' momentum in the opposite direction. But their velocities are equal and opposite only if they are both of exactly the same mass.

If, for example, both have a mass of 150 lbs., and they push each other apart so that they are travelling at 11 feet per second, then the momentum of each is (mass × velocity) or 150 × 11 lbs. feet per second (which is 1,650 lbs. feet per second). The momentum of one skater is *plus* 1,650 lbs. feet per second, and the momentum of the other is *minus* 1,650 lbs. feet per second. Momentum has been conserved.

However, if one skater has a mass of 100 lbs. and the other a mass of 200 lbs., then it is found that they do not

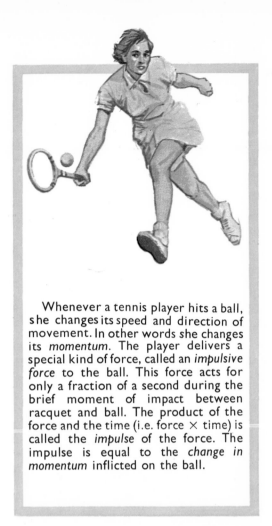

Whenever a tennis player hits a ball, she changes its speed and direction of movement. In other words she changes its *momentum*. The player delivers a special kind of force, called an *impulsive force* to the ball. This force acts for only a fraction of a second during the brief moment of impact between racquet and ball. The product of the force and the time (i.e. force × time) is called the *impulse* of the force. The impulse is equal to the *change in momentum* inflicted on the ball.

travel with equal and opposite velocities. The 100-lbs. skater may travel away at 15 feet per second. His momentum is 1,500 lbs. feet per second. But the velocity of the 200-lbs. skater is smaller. His velocity is only $7\frac{1}{2}$ feet per second, in the opposite direction.

The two momenta must balance each other. In this example, both must have momenta of 1,500 lbs. feet per second. The two *velocities* need not be equal and opposite, nor need the kinetic energies of the two skaters be equal. It happens that the momentum is the one quantity which balances when movements are suddenly changed.

A skater starts her spin with arms outstretched. She swings both her arms around to give her body the necessary starting impulse. Slowly she starts to spin.

Then, to speed the spin, she pulls her arms tightly in to her body. With no extra effort, she spins much faster.

As she twisted her whole body around, the skater gave herself *angular momentum*. *Momentum* is a word used to describe the quantity of motion, when the body is moving in a straight line. It is equal to mass multiplied by

Momentum and Angular Momentum

Momentum equals mass times velocity, but angular momentum is not equal to mass times angular velocity. When something is spinning, different parts of it rotate at different velocities. Those parts farthest away from the spinning axis move the quickest. The quantity which determines the angular momentum and which takes into account the distance away from the spinning axis, is called the *moment of inertia*. Angular momentum is equal to moment of inertia multiplied by angular velocity.

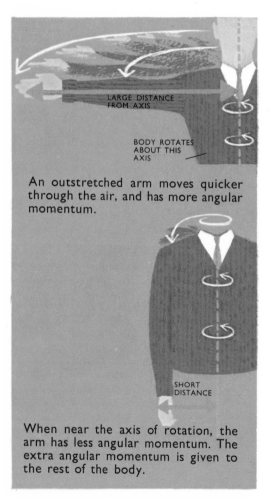

An outstretched arm moves quicker through the air, and has more angular momentum.

When near the axis of rotation, the arm has less angular momentum. The extra angular momentum is given to the rest of the body.

velocity. *Angular momentum* is the quantity of spinning motion. It depends, among other things, on the *angular velocity* of the skater, a measure of the number of spins per second.

The skater's outstretched arms are farthest away from the rest of her body. They are moving quickest through the air. Consequently, they have more momentum, and more angular momentum.

The total amount of angular momentum remains the same after the skater has pulled in her arms. Angular momentum is one of the quantities in physics which is *conserved*. Angular momentum with arms outstretched equals angular momentum with arms alongside body.

The sudden increase in the rate of spin comes about when the extra angular momentum of the spinning arms is shared out over her whole body. Angular momentum lost by the arms is gained by the rest of the skater's body, which gains 'more angular motion' and spins quicker.

Friction

CHAPTER NINETEEN

Friction

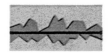

To understand why one solid does not slide easily over another it is only necessary to look at the surface of a solid under a high power microscope. Even an apparently smooth piece of metal is seen to have tiny irregular 'hills and valleys' all over its surface (diagram left). When two such surfaces are rubbed together the 'peaks' of one dovetail with those of the other so it is not surprising that movement is hindered.

If the surfaces are *lubricated* by inserting a film of liquid between them, their irregularities are covered up by the film and they can slide fairly easily (diagram right).

The most common lubricants are oils and grease, but graphite, a solid, is also important. Graphite is a form of carbon in which the atoms are arranged in layers. Neighbouring layers can slide over each other with very little friction.

When a sledge is pushed over ice, the pressure under the runners melts the ice so that the sledge actually lubricates itself with a thin film of water as it slides along.

The patterned 'tread' on a car tyre is primarily intended to improve its grip on wet and greasy roads. A smooth tyre cannot make contact with the wet surface. because of the layer of water trapped beneath it acting as a lubricant. But a patterned tread has a number of small areas of rubber with spaces between them. Each 'diamond' of the tread makes contact with the road surface by squeezing the water into these spaces.

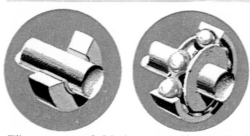

The amount of friction set up by a wheel turning on its axle can be considerably reduced by the use of balls or rollers.

ANYONE trying to push a boat over a dry, level beach meets with a considerable opposition. The force which tends to oppose every sliding movement between solids is called the force of friction. Friction is an important feature of everyday life. We could not, for example, walk along a road unless our feet could grip on its surface. The brakes of a bicycle or automobile use the friction between fixed ' brake blocks ' and the moving wheel to slow it down. Of course this effect is not always an advantage. Friction between moving parts on a vehicle is one of the main causes of wear.

The force of friction between two solids does not depend upon their areas. This may seem surprising unless we recall that even highly polished surfaces are really like miniature mountain ranges. They only make contact with each other in the very few places where the peaks of one rest on the peaks of the other. The force of friction between two solids does depend upon how hard they are pressed together. In the case of an object resting on a horizontal surface the frictional force which opposes any attempt to make it slide is directly proportional to the weight of the object. In other words the ratio of the frictional force to the load is constant. This ratio is known as the coefficient of sliding friction. It varies from one pair of substances to another. (See p. 12.)

The friction involved in *rolling* is less than the friction involved in *sliding*. Hence it is much easier to roll

An oxen-drawn sledge in Madeira. When the driver wants to turn a corner he puts a greasy sack under one of the runners. The friction on that side is reduced and the whole sledge slews round.

a log along the ground than to drag it. This explains why the wheel forms such a useful part of practically all land vehicles. For the same reason ball-bearings and roller-bearings serve to make movement easier and to reduce wear in machinery.

The energy spent in overcoming the resistance of frictional forces is turned into heat. The primitive method of starting a fire by rubbing two sticks together provides a convincing example of this. The heat produced by the friction between a space capsule and the atmosphere as it returns to Earth has proved to be one of the astronauts' major hazards.

The frictional force opposing movement between the molecules of liquids or gases is known as *viscosity*.

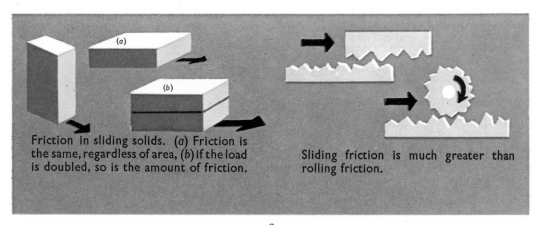

Friction in sliding solids. (*a*) Friction is the same, regardless of area, (*b*) if the load is doubled, so is the amount of friction.

Sliding friction is much greater than rolling friction.

CHAPTER TWENTY

Bearings and Lubrication

IF the moving parts of a machine are not lubricated at regular intervals the machine will not function satisfactorily. Eventually the machine will grind to a halt because of the lack of oil. An extreme instance is the seizing up of an internal combustion engine in which the moving parts have become dry and overheated.

(Left): An enlarged section through dry bearings showing irregularities. (Right): Oil film separating the surfaces.

Application of oil or grease reduces the frictional forces which exist between the rotating shafts, spindles or wheels, and the fixed supports and thus enables their surfaces to slide easily over one another. Whereas a pair of dry surfaces will 'bite' into one another, even if they are comparatively smooth, the presence of a thin film of lubricant between the stationary and moving surfaces enables the surfaces to 'float' one on the other. The slight irregularities in one surface are kept clear of the imperfections of the other surface by the film of lubricant.

A rotating shaft needs to be supported at, or close to, its ends. If it is long additional supports or bearings may be needed at intermediate points as well. The simplest form of bearing, which is quite satisfactory if the speed is low and if the only forces acting on the bearing are perpendicular to the shaft, is the *journal* type. In this type the shaft is supported by a close-fitting hollow cylinder called a *shell* or *bush*. As the bush may be subject to considerable wear, it is made so that it can be easily replaced in the bearing *housing*.

Lack of oil between the bearing bush and the shaft results in a considerable increase in the frictional forces acting between the surfaces. This, in turn, generates heat which causes the metal to expand and eventually the bearing seizes up. As serious damage to the machine would result from bearing seizure, it is usual to line the bushes of such bearings with a soft alloy which has a fairly low melting point. In this way the bearing melts when it becomes overheated thus avoiding damage to the shaft or whatever the shaft is driving. The low melting point alloys come within the general classification of *white metal*.

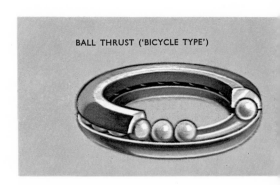

BALL THRUST ('BICYCLE TYPE')

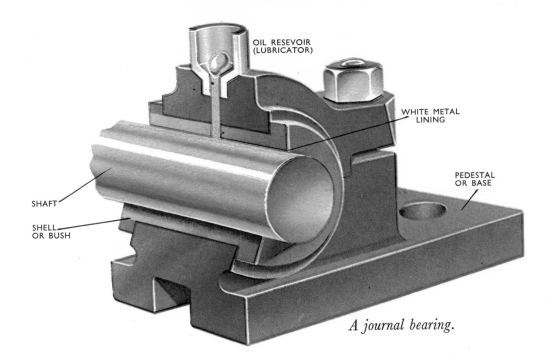

OIL RESEVOIR
(LUBRICATOR)

WHITE METAL
LINING

PEDESTAL
OR BASE

SHAFT

SHELL
OR BUSH

A journal bearing.

There are two different types of white metal, the typical compositions of which are tin 88%, antimony 8%, and copper 4%; and lead 80%, antimony 14% and tin 6%.

In order that the bearings do not have to be lubricated too frequently, it is necessary to incorporate into their design a means of holding a reserve of oil. This is usually done by having grooves cut in the surface of the bush, and also by having a small reservoir of oil above the bearing so that it can flow down and be distributed over the surface of the rotating shaft as it is required. There are sometimes great pressures acting between the bearing and the shaft, in which case lubricants have to be forced in under pressure.

Ball and Roller Bearings

More satisfactory bearings are the *ball* and *roller* types. In these the moving shaft and the fixed bearing housing are separated by balls or rollers, which run in grooves or *races* set in the surface of the shaft and the housing. The main advantage of these types of bearing over the journal type, is that the sliding friction between the surfaces of the rotating shaft and the fixed bush has

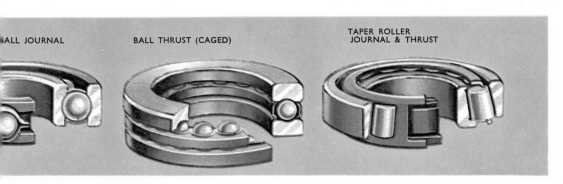

BALL JOURNAL

BALL THRUST (CAGED)

TAPER ROLLER
JOURNAL & THRUST

63

been replaced by rolling friction between the balls or rollers and each of the two surfaces. The loss of energy in overcoming rolling friction is much less than that required to counteract sliding friction.

Ball bearings were first used towards the end of the nineteenth century and found favour in the construction of the bicycle which was then becoming popular. In the original ball bearings the balls completely filled the space between the two races, but it is now usual to have the balls separated by a metal cage. This serves to keep the balls evenly spaced around the race and prevents uneven wear.

For these bearings to function satisfactorily, it is necessary that the balls or rollers and the races are made from good quality hardened steel and that they are manufactured to a high degree of accuracy. In particular, it is most important that all the balls in one race are of the same size exactly.

There is a large range of types of ball and roller bearings which have been developed to suit various applications, and a few are illustrated. Roller bearings are used where there is a large force between the surfaces. Tapered roller bearings are useful where there is a thrust along the shaft.

CHAPTER TWENTY-ONE

Clutches

A CLUTCH is a kind of mechanical switch. It is fitted between the *driving* shaft and the *driven* shaft in any machine where the engine continues to rotate whether the actual machinery is operating or not. The simplest form of clutch is the dog-

clutch, in which the shaft connected to the engine and the ends of the shaft connected to the wheels dovetail into each other. It can connect only when the two shafts are moving at the same speed.

This is, however, no use for the main clutch in, say, an internal combustion engine which relies on the *continuous* movement of pistons and crankshaft. The engine will not run below a certain speed, so the clutch must connect the driving shaft to the driven shaft gradually until both shafts rotate at the same speed.

One type of clutch is known as the *single dry plate friction clutch*, although in fact three plates (flywheel, friction plate and pressure plate) are involved in the transmission of power. The 'single' plate carries two flat, ring-shaped linings of

DOG CLUTCH

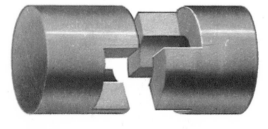

The two shafts fit into each other, and can be connected only when both are moving at the same speed.

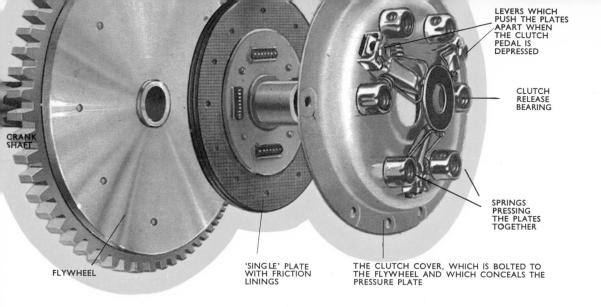

LEVERS WHICH
PUSH THE PLATES
APART WHEN
THE CLUTCH
PEDAL IS
DEPRESSED

CLUTCH
RELEASE
BEARING

SPRINGS
PRESSING
THE PLATES
TOGETHER

CRANK
SHAFT

FLYWHEEL

'SINGLE' PLATE
WITH FRICTION
LININGS

THE CLUTCH COVER, WHICH IS BOLTED TO
THE FLYWHEEL AND WHICH CONCEALS THE
PRESSURE PLATE

A 'single' dry plate friction clutch. Normally the three plates are pressed tightly together. When the clutch pedal is depressed they move a fraction of an inch apart.

an asbestos material, similar to brake linings, one on each side. It is sandwiched between the flywheel (which is of course firmly bolted to the crankshaft) on one side and a *pressure plate* on the other side. The whole is enclosed by a sort of soup plate, the clutch cover. Between the pressure plate and the clutch cover are strong springs which push the plate vigorously towards the flywheel, providing the pressure which normally squashes the three plates together. A system of levers connects the pressure plate, through the *clutch thrust ring*, to the foot-operated clutch pedal. These levers act against the springs, and by pressing down or letting back the clutch pedal the pressure on the plates can be relieved or applied gradually.

When the engine is disconnected the plates lie only a fraction of an inch apart. As the pressure is applied by the springs, when the clutch pedal is allowed to rise, and the plates are brought into contact, friction between the flywheel and one clutch lining grips the middle friction plate, and rotates it. Then friction between the clutch lining and the pressure plate causes the shaft connected to the wheels to rotate. When the pressure is small the plates will slip against each other, but as the pressure is increased gradually and the load starts moving there will be less slipping until all plates are tightly pressed together and rotate at the same speed.

Friction converts some of the mechanical energy into heat, which must be radiated or conducted away from the two outer plates. Generally speaking, the larger the clutch, the more power it can transmit without overheating. If the clutch does overheat, the linings may burn or even act as a lubricant, making the transmission of power incomplete.

CHAPTER TWENTY-TWO

Brakes

IN a car, heat energy generated by the burning of petrol is converted into mechanical, or kinetic, energy to accelerate the car and keep it moving. The brakes do the reverse. They reconvert the mechanical energy, by means of friction, into heat, and so slow the car down.

In conventional drum-braking systems the movement of the foot-pedal is transmitted, either mechanically or, in the more usual *hydraulic* brakes, through pipes containing a special fluid, to each of the wheels. Rotating with each wheel is the *brake drum*, a hollow metal cylinder. Inside the drum, but fixed so that they do not rotate, are the brake shoes, each of which has a separate lining. The shoes are coupled to the movement of

The hydraulic braking system of a car fitted with conventional drum brakes. When the brake pedal is depressed, the pressure in the braking fluid forces the brake shoes against the drums and slows the car down.

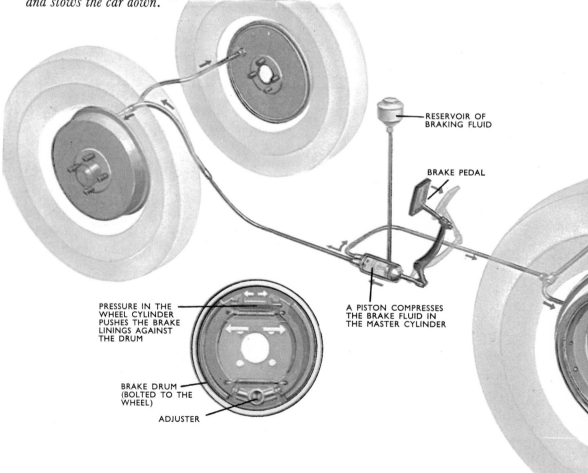

RESERVOIR OF BRAKING FLUID

BRAKE PEDAL

PRESSURE IN THE WHEEL CYLINDER PUSHES THE BRAKE LININGS AGAINST THE DRUM

A PISTON COMPRESSES THE BRAKE FLUID IN THE MASTER CYLINDER

BRAKE DRUM (BOLTED TO THE WHEEL)

ADJUSTER

the brake pedal, so that when the pedal is depressed, the linings press against the rotating drum. The friction between the two surfaces tends to slow down the rotary movement of the wheel. The brakes are effective (i.e. in converting mechanical energy into heat) only when one of the two surfaces, the lining and the drum, is rotating and rubbing against the other.

Because of the rubbing action against the drum, the brake linings are subject to wear and tear. They are made from asbestos fabric which, besides giving a good braking effect (having a high coefficient of friction),

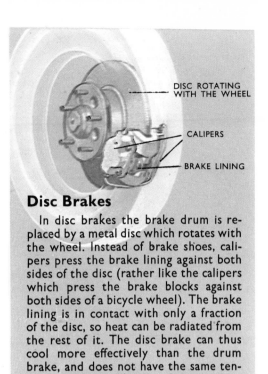

DISC ROTATING WITH THE WHEEL

CALIPERS

BRAKE LINING

Disc Brakes

In disc brakes the brake drum is replaced by a metal disc which rotates with the wheel. Instead of brake shoes, calipers press the brake lining against both sides of the disc (rather like the calipers which press the brake blocks against both sides of a bicycle wheel). The brake lining is in contact with only a fraction of the disc, so heat can be radiated from the rest of it. The disc brake can thus cool more effectively than the drum brake, and does not have the same tendency to 'fade'. The use of the disc also gives a steadier, more consistent braking force.

also happens to be a very good insulator of heat. This means that the heat generated by friction cannot escape from the brakes through the linings. Nor can it easily escape from the brake drums, which are practically enclosed. Thus the brakes become very hot—even red-hot in extreme cases—after they have been used for any length of time. The brake lining must be able to withstand high temperatures, otherwise it may decompose, or melt, and instead of stopping the wheel, even act as a lubricant. In this case, the braking power would disappear—this effect being commonly known as *brake fade*. When the brake has cooled, the frictional characteristics of the linings usually revert to normal. Brake fade may also be caused by the expansion of the drum with heat.

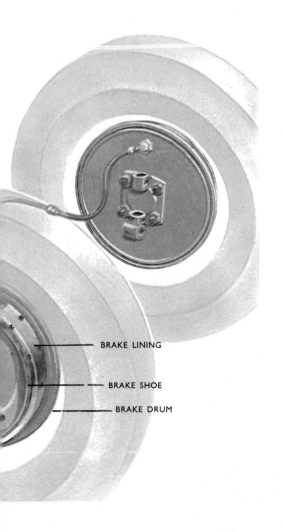

BRAKE LINING

BRAKE SHOE

BRAKE DRUM

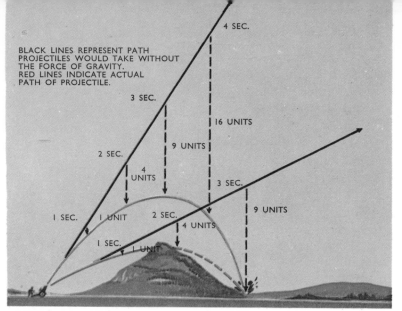

BLACK LINES REPRESENT PATH PROJECTILES WOULD TAKE WITHOUT THE FORCE OF GRAVITY.
RED LINES INDICATE ACTUAL PATH OF PROJECTILE.

4 SEC.

3 SEC.

16 UNITS

9 UNITS

2 SEC.

4 UNITS

3 SEC.

1 SEC.   1 UNIT   2 SEC.   9 UNITS

4 UNITS

1 SEC.   1 UNIT

The motion of the projectile is regarded as being made up of an unchanging motion in the direction it was projected and free fall from a line drawn in that direction. The motion in the original direction being of uniform velocity, the distance travelled is directly proportional to the time, i.e., the distance travelled in two seconds is double that travelled in one second.

The fall from the line drawn in the original direction is with uniform acceleration; therefore, the distance travelled is proportional to the square of the time, i.e. the distance travelled in two seconds is four times the distance travelled in one second.

For any given distance there are two angles of elevation which will land the shell at that point. A practical application of this is that the higher of the two trajectories might be needed for a shell to clear an intervening ridge.

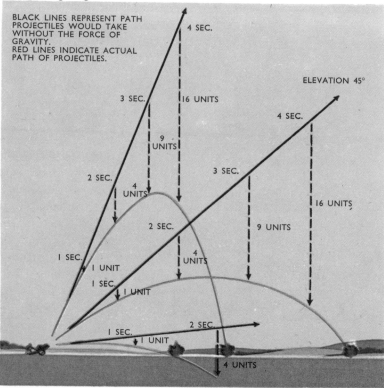

BLACK LINES REPRESENT PATH PROJECTILES WOULD TAKE WITHOUT THE FORCE OF GRAVITY.
RED LINES INDICATE ACTUAL PATH OF PROJECTILES.

4 SEC.

ELEVATION 45°

3 SEC.   16 UNITS

4 SEC.

9 UNITS

2 SEC.   3 SEC.

4 UNITS

2 SEC.   16 UNITS

1 SEC.   9 UNITS

1 UNIT   4 UNITS

1 SEC.

1 UNIT

2 SEC.

1 SEC.   1 UNIT

4 UNITS

The maximum range of a gun is obtained, in theory, by elevating the barrel to an angle of 45° above the horizontal. In practice the angle might be slightly greater because the lack of forward movement would be compensated by less air resistance (the density of the air decreases with height). Below: the trajectory of a rocket is extremely difficult to calculate for it accelerates to its maximum velocity while in flight.

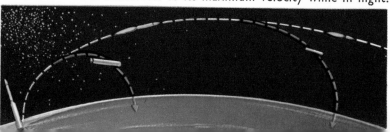

Gravity and Gyroscopes

CHAPTER TWENTY-THREE

Weight and Mass

WEIGHT and mass are probably the two most badly treated words in the language of science. They are so closely related to one another that under normal circumstances, both the weight and mass of an object are numerically exactly the same. 10 lb of potatoes will have a weight of 10 lb

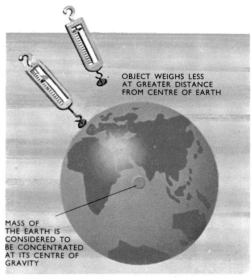

OBJECT WEIGHS LESS
AT GREATER DISTANCE
FROM CENTRE OF EARTH

MASS OF
THE EARTH IS
CONSIDERED TO
BE CONCENTRATED
AT ITS CENTRE OF
GRAVITY

The weight of a body is a measure of the force of attraction between it and the Earth. The greater the distance between a body and the centre of gravity of the Earth the less it weighs.

FORCE
PRESSING
DOWN

COMPRESSION
IS INDICATED
ON DIAL

LEVER SYSTEM
CONNECTS SPRING
TO DIAL

SPRING IS
COMPRESSED

Weight is being measured. This is the force with which the body pushes down on the spring. The amount the spring is compressed is measured by a system of levers.

force and a mass of 10 lb. The values are the same and the words falsely appear to be interchangeable.

If the potatoes have been weighed with an instrument working off the extension of a spring (the more a spring extends, the heavier is the object), then the *weight* is being found. The potatoes are 10 lb. force, not 10 lb.

When the potatoes are put in the pan of the instrument, the spring offers an upward pull to the pan and its contents in an attempt to stop itself from stretching. Gravitational forces acting on the potatoes try to pull them down and make them fall. The spring extends until these two opposing forces exactly balance each other and then the weight can be read off as a measure of the extension. The spring is obviously measuring the size of the force trying to extend it and therefore weight must be a kind of force.

This downward pull on the potatoes depends upon two things – the amount of substance or matter contained in the potatoes and the gravitational pull of the Earth. It makes no difference where the potatoes are taken. Unless bits are chopped off them they are always composed of the same amount of matter, but the Earth's gravitational *field* (the pull the Earth will exert on a body) does vary. A stone dropped down a well will have an increased velocity of 32 ft/sec for every second it falls. If it falls out of a satellite in orbit, miles up in the sky, then in 1 second the increase in velocity is considerably less. This is because the stone is further away from the Earth and therefore influenced less by it. As the Earth's gravitational field changes, so does the weight of an object. Using a spring instrument, the potatoes will weigh slightly less on a mountain top than they will at sea level.

But mass is something that never varies. It is the amount of matter a

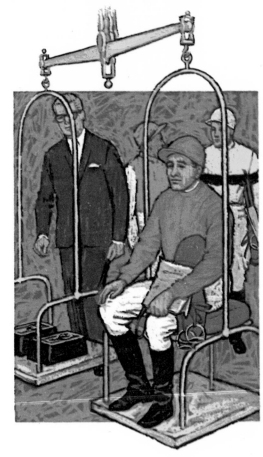

Mass is being measured. The mass of the jockey is exactly balanced by the masses placed on the other pan. Equal pulls will be exerted on both pans irrespective of the size of the gravitational field.

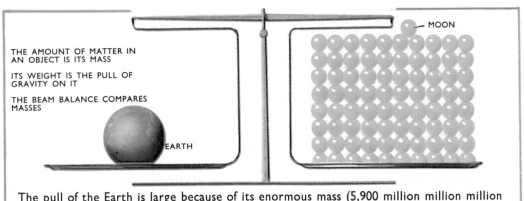

THE AMOUNT OF MATTER IN AN OBJECT IS ITS MASS

ITS WEIGHT IS THE PULL OF GRAVITY ON IT

THE BEAM BALANCE COMPARES MASSES

EARTH

MOON

The pull of the Earth is large because of its enormous mass (5,900 million million million tons). Because the Moon is a much smaller mass, its gravitational pull is much smaller. The mass of the Earth is about 81 times that of the Moon.

substance has in it. A block of lead will be composed of a particular number of atoms. An atom has 82 protons, 126 neutrons and 82 electrons. In other words, each atom has a certain amount of matter in it. It does not matter if the block of lead is down a well, up a mountain or on the surface of the Moon, provided nothing has been chopped off it or stuck on it, it has the same matter in it and therefore the same mass.

Because of this, mass has to be measured using an instrument which will give the same answer wherever it is used. The beam balance is used to measure mass. The object of unknown mass is placed on the left hand balance pan. The pan drops and the beam tilts because there is nothing on the other pan to balance it. Metal 'weights' (badly named – they should be called masses) are placed on the other pan until a balance is achieved – mass is balanced against mass. When the balance is taken to a place where the gravitational field is much less, there is less pull on the object, but also equally less pull on the 'weights' in the other pan, and the same result is obtained.

CHAPTER TWENTY-FOUR

Gravitation

EVERYONE knows that objects fall downwards (i.e. towards the centre of the Earth) when they are dropped. They are said to be pulled down by the "force of gravity". Sir Isaac Newton is alleged to have "discovered" the force of gravity when he saw an apple fall to the ground (in some versions of what is in any case an improbable story, the apple fell on Newton as it travelled Earthwards). Actually the fact that the Earth tends to pull objects to it was already well known before Newton's time. What Newton did "discover" was that the Earth is not unique in tending to pull objects to it. *Every* object tends to pull every other

Specks of matter (left) *suspended in free space, will eventually be drawn together* (right) *by the gravitational forces which they exert on each other.*

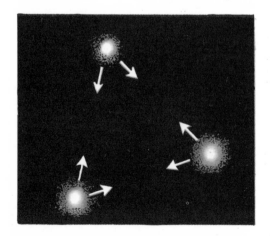

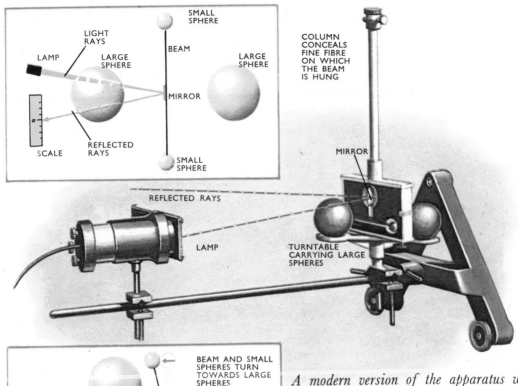

The illustration shows labels including:

SMALL SPHERE · LIGHT RAYS · LAMP · LARGE SPHERE · BEAM · LARGE SPHERE · MIRROR · SCALE · REFLECTED RAYS · SMALL SPHERE · COLUMN CONCEALS FINE FIBRE ON WHICH THE BEAM IS HUNG · MIRROR · REFLECTED RAYS · LAMP · TURNTABLE CARRYING LARGE SPHERES · BEAM AND SMALL SPHERES TURN TOWARDS LARGE SPHERES · LARGE SPHERES MOVED TO NEW POSITION · REFLECTED BEAM SHIFTS TO NEW POSITION

A modern version of the apparatus with which Cavendish measured the attraction between masses. At the start of the experiment (top inset) the large spheres are set at right angles to the beam carrying the small spheres so that the attractions between the small spheres and each of the large spheres exactly cancel one another. When the large spheres are swung out of the perpendicular position (bottom inset) the attractions no longer cancel and the beam twists round slightly. The force of attraction between the pairs of spheres is equal to the torsion (resistance to twisting) of the fibre supporting the beam, and hence can be calculated from the angle through which the beam moves.

object to it. In other words there is a force of attraction between every pair of objects in the Universe. Whether the objects are invisible specks of matter or giant stars, the force of attraction between them always obeys the same law. This law, known as Newton's law of gravitation, states that the force of attraction between two objects is directly proportional to the product of their masses (i.e. the masses multiplied together) and inversely proportional

to the square of the distance between them (i.e. proportional to $\frac{1}{\text{distance} \times \text{distance}}$. The distance is measured between the centres of the objects. Suppose that gravitational attraction between two objects placed one inch apart is equal to a force of one pound force. If the objects are moved so

The theory of gravitation was first worked out by Sir Isaac Newton. He compared the motion of the Moon with that of a bullet shot from a very high mountain. If the bullet were given sufficient velocity the curve of its fall would follow the curvature of the Earth. Newton drew a diagram similar to the one shown here to illustrate his idea.

From the earlier work of Kepler he was able to show that an inverse square law of force would account for the observed motions of the planets round the Sun. A similar law ought, therefore, he argued, account for the motion of the Moon round the Earth. If gravity obeyed an inverse square law then this motion could be explained by the inward attraction of gravity in just the same way that the circular motion of a stone whirling round a boy's head is caused by the inward tension in the string.

Knowing the distance of the Moon from the Earth and the time taken for it to rotate once he was able to work out the force needed. He compared this with the force of gravity at the Earth's surface and found that it did, in fact, obey the inverse square law.

Newton successfully applied his theory to many problems including the motions of comets and the cause of tides on the seas. In this way he was able to show that a gravitational attraction exists between all objects as well as between the Moon and the Earth and between the planets and the Sun.

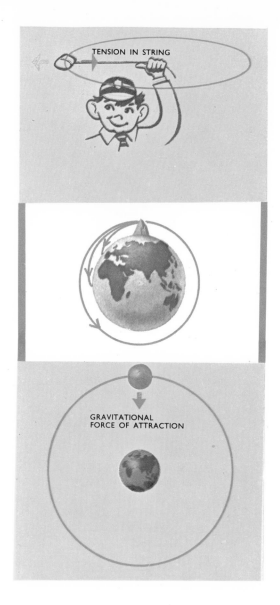

that they are two inches apart the force of attraction will be reduced to one-quarter of one pound weight. If the objects are placed ten inches apart the force of attraction will be only one-hundredth of one pound weight. In reality gravitation is a very small force, except when it is concerned with immense objects such as planets, and it is therefore difficult to measure by experiment. Just over one hundred years after Newton's law of gravitation

was published, Henry Cavendish did succeed in measuring the tiny force of attraction between two pairs of lead balls. Newton's law of gravitation together with Cavendish's numerical results make it possible to calculate the mass and average density of the Earth. Cavendish's figures must have been surprisingly accurate, for his calculation of the Earth's density erred by only one per cent. Since then, many similar experiments have

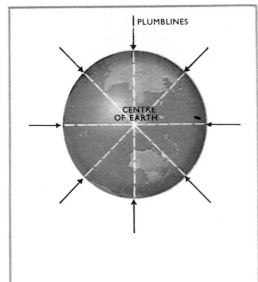

If plumblines were hung above the Earth's surface and their paths were continued into the Earth, they would all meet at the centre of the Earth. This point is its centre of gravity. The Earth behaves as if all its mass is concentrated at its centre and attracts things in the direction of this point.

pound weight. Gravitation is always a force of attraction, never a force of repulsion. In this respect it is very different from the forces in magnetism or electricity. But although no completely acceptable explanation of this mysterious force has been put forward so far, its important effects are well known. It is worth remembering that gravitation holds the planets in their fixed orbits.

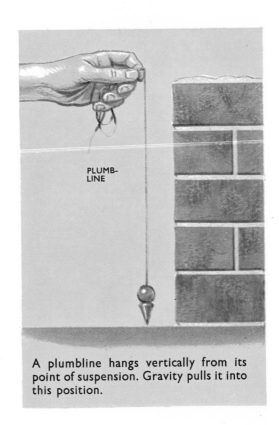

A plumbline hangs vertically from its point of suspension. Gravity pulls it into this position.

shown that masses attract each other with a force equal to about one fifteen-millionth of their masses (in grams) multiplied together, divided by the square of the distance between them (in centimetres). Suppose two ships, each of ten thousand tons, floated with their centres just over one hundred yards apart; according to this calculation, the force of attraction would be less than one-quarter of one

CHAPTER TWENTY-FIVE

How Fast does it Fall?

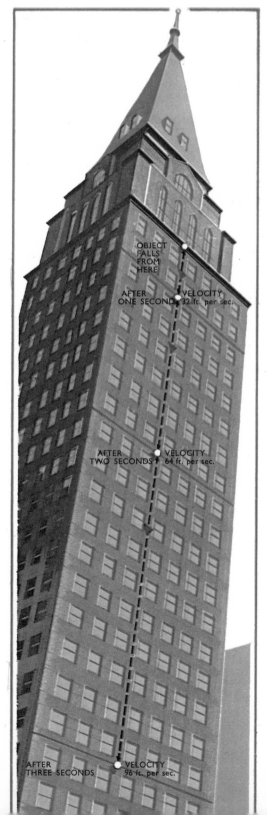

OBJECTS FALLS FROM HERE

AFTER ONE SECOND — VELOCITY 32 ft. per sec.

AFTER TWO SECONDS — VELOCITY 64 ft. per sec.

AFTER THREE SECONDS — VELOCITY 96 ft. per sec.

OBJECTS move because a force is acting on them, pushing or pulling them. They fall because the force of gravity pulls them towards Earth. Forces tend to make objects accelerate (speed up), and gravity is no exception. A stone dropped over a cliff, for example, accelerates at roughly 32 feet per second per second. This means that each second the stone moves 32 feet per second faster than the second before. The easiest way to explain this is to consider how fast the stone is travelling at different times.

To begin with the stone is stationary at 0 feet per second. At the end of 1 second it is travelling at 32 feet per second. At the end of 2 seconds it moves at 64 feet per second, at 3 seconds 96 feet per second and so on. In fact every second it travels 32 feet per second faster.

Because of the air resistance experienced by *all* objects as they fall the acceleration will always be slightly reduced. Only in a vacuum are the figures quoted exactly true.

Whenever a steady force is applied to an object this produces an acceleration. For example, a wheelbarrow pushed over a smooth road with a steady force moves faster and faster. An object falling freely under the influence of gravity does so with an acceleration of 32 ft./sec./sec. If it starts from rest, at the end of the first second of its fall it has a velocity of 32 ft./sec., after 2 seconds 64 ft./sec. and after 3 seconds a velocity of 96 ft./ sec.

76

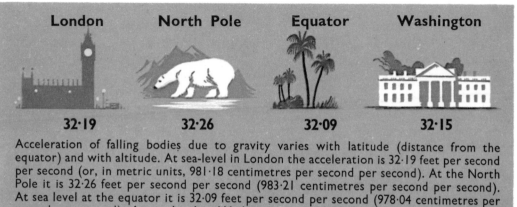

London	North Pole	Equator	Washington
32·19	32·26	32·09	32·15

Acceleration of falling bodies due to gravity varies with latitude (distance from the equator) and with altitude. At sea-level in London the acceleration is 32·19 feet per second per second (or, in metric units, 981·18 centimetres per second per second). At the North Pole it is 32·26 feet per second per second (983·21 centimetres per second per second). At sea level at the equator it is 32·09 feet per second per second (978·04 centimetres per second per second). At sea level in Washington it is 32·15 feet per second per second (980·08 centimetres per second per second).

CHAPTER TWENTY-SIX

Pendulums

A PENDULUM swinging under gravity from a fixed point marks out equal intervals of time. This fact, first observed by Galileo in the Cathedral at Pisa, enabled him to design the first pendulum clock. Galileo, looking at the chandeliers became aware that the time of oscillation did not depend on the distance of swing. The credit for the general use of pendulums in clocks goes to the great Dutch physicist Christian Huygens, who spent a great part of his life on this subject. Pendulums nowadays are employed in clocks, mining surveys and in the metronome used by students of music.

The Simple and Compound Pendulum

There are various different types of pendulums. Two sorts of common pendulums are the *simple pendulum*, which is just a bob swinging at the end of a length of string, and the rigid *compound pendulum*. The period of oscillation of a simple pendulum, i.e. the time to swing from one side to the other and back again is $2\pi\sqrt{\dfrac{l}{g}}$ where l is the length of the string and g the acceleration due to gravity (the acceleration of a falling stone) at the

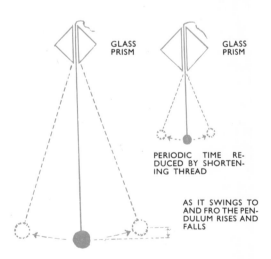

GLASS PRISM

GLASS PRISM

PERIODIC TIME RE-DUCED BY SHORTEN-ING THREAD

AS IT SWINGS TO AND FRO THE PEN-DULUM RISES AND FALLS

The time of swing of a simple pendulum of given length is constant, but if the thread is shortened the periodic time is reduced.

77

Christian Huygens' Correction

Unfortunately the calculated values of the period of swing of the ideal simple and compound pendulums are only correct assuming that the arcs of swing are very small. More complex calculation shows that the period of the pendulum depends on the length of the arc of swing. As soon as there is a variation in this length, an error is introduced. Christian Huygens investigated the mathematics of the finite arc of swing and discovered that if the top end of a pendulum was flexible and wrapped itself around a cycloidal shape (a cycloidal shape is that curve traced out by a point on a rolling circle), the dependence of the period on the length of swing was removed, and the pendulum would always keep exact time. He designed a clock on these principles but it was not built in his time.

the force which tips the escapement wheel in pendulum clocks, a simple pendulum which is without rigidity would be no use so a rigid *compound pendulum* is the type used.

An easily constructed compound pendulum is a long metal tube with holes bored in it at equal intervals. The pendulum is balanced on a knife edge at these holes. As the point of suspension is moved towards the centre of the tube (the centre of gravity) the period of oscillation diminishes and then starts to increase again. This means that there is a certain distance from the centre of gravity at which the period of oscillation is a minimum. If the pendulum is hung the other way up, the same point can be found on the other side. The minimum period of oscillation of the compound pendulum is the same as that of a simple pendulum the length of which is the distance between these two points.

The Time of Swing Depends on the Length

The period of a pendulum depends directly on its length. Any variation in temperature could change the length and alter the period. In clocks this problem is overcome in different ways. Large church clocks often have wooden connecting rods for their

Earth's surface. At a place where g is much smaller, such as on the Moon, the period will be longer and pendulum clocks will go slow. This is because when g is smaller $2\pi\sqrt{\dfrac{l}{g}}$ is larger. The dependence of the period on g provides a useful way for checking gravity on the surface of the Earth. To provide

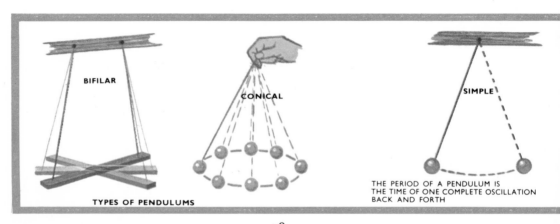

BIFILAR

CONICAL

SIMPLE

THE PERIOD OF A PENDULUM IS THE TIME OF ONE COMPLETE OSCILLATION BACK AND FORTH

TYPES OF PENDULUMS

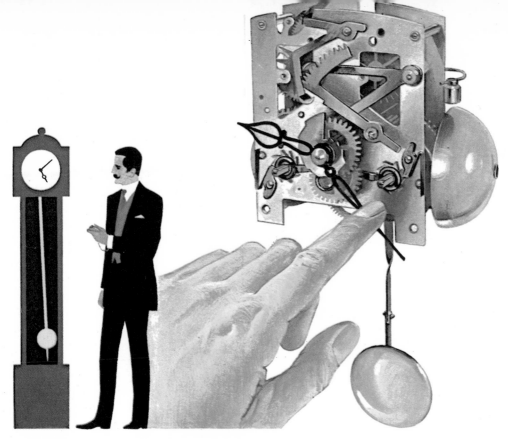

In measuring the same time interval the short pendulum of the mantelpiece clock moves to and fro more often than the longer pendulum of the grandfather clock.

pendulums. Wood expands little with heat. Often a *compensated pendulum*, which depends on the different expansions with heat of different materials is used in clocks. Though the connecting rod may expand with heat and lower, the bob (or its support) expands upwards. The net result is that the length of the bob from the pendulum suspension does not change.

The Foucault Pendulum

One of the most celebrated historical pendulums is the one invented by Charles Foucault in 1851, to show the rotation of the Earth. An iron ball is hung at the end of a 200-foot steel

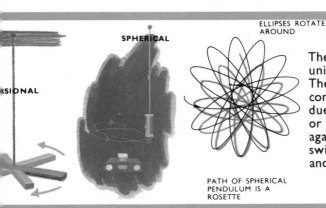

SPHERICAL

ELLIPSES ROTATE AROUND

SIONAL

PATH OF SPHERICAL PENDULUM IS A ROSETTE

The motion of a pendulum illustrates the universal law of Conservation of Energy. The kinetic energy (energy of motion) is converted into potential energy (energy due to the position of the pendulum bob or to the twist in the wire) and back again. The energy is used up as the bob swings in overcoming friction of the air and eventually the pendulum stops.

wire. It is then drawn aside and tied with a thread in that position. The thread is burned through and the pendulum starts swinging slowly. The heavy pendulum maintains its original direction of swing and the Earth rotates underneath it. One of these pendulums at the North Pole if it kept swinging, would do a complete revolution in 24 hours; in London it would take 30 hours 40 minutes. At the Equator it will not appear to rotate at all. In the Northern Hemisphere it rotates clockwise; in the Southern Hemisphere anti-clockwise. In fact the number of degrees it appears to turn through per hour, at any place on the Earth, is the *sine* of the angle of latitude multiplied by 15.

The Spherical Pendulum

A ball swinging around in a circle at

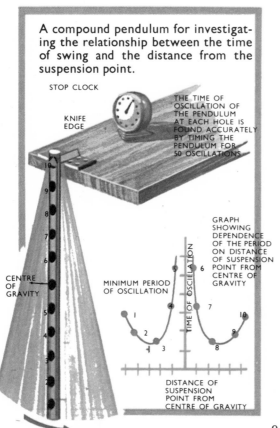

A compound pendulum for investigating the relationship between the time of swing and the distance from the suspension point.

STOP CLOCK

KNIFE EDGE

THE TIME OF OSCILLATION OF THE PENDULUM AT EACH HOLE IS FOUND ACCURATELY BY TIMING THE PENDULUM FOR 50 OSCILLATIONS

CENTRE OF GRAVITY

GRAPH SHOWING DEPENDENCE OF THE PERIOD ON DISTANCE OF SUSPENSION POINT FROM CENTRE OF GRAVITY

MINIMUM PERIOD OF OSCILLATION

TIME OF OSCILLATION

DISTANCE OF SUSPENSION POINT FROM CENTRE OF GRAVITY

AS THE EARTH ROTATES THE PENDULUM STAYS SWINGING IN THE SAME DIRECTION

Foucault's pendulum in the Pantheon in Paris.

the end of a string is called a *Conical pendulum*. A conical pendulum of a certain length has the same period of oscillation as a simple pendulum of the same length. Both of these pendulums are special examples of the *spherical pendulum* – a ball on a string swinging around in an ellipse. A straight line (the simple pendulum) and a circle (the conical pendulum) are both extreme kinds of elipses.

One of the interesting motions of this pendulum is barely noticeable. As the ball swings around in ellipses, the ellipses rotate and start to trace out a rosette pattern. This interesting phenomenon can be photographed by means of a small torch swinging on a long string over a camera in a darkened room. The actual gradual turning around of the ellipses is very slight, compared with the backwards and forwards oscillatory motion.

Care must be taken in starting a Foucault pendulum because if it is accidentally given the slightest side-ways motion it becomes a spherical pendulum and will trace out an elliptical path. The turning around of the ellipses will then mask the rotation due to the earth. This is why it is started by burning a thread with a match so as to make it swing in one plane.

The *torsional pendulum* is called a pendulum but it does not depend on gravity. It is a heavy body spinning back and forth at the end of a long wire, and can be used in the laboratory to find the resistance to twisting of the material of the wire. A bar swinging from two parallel strings at its ends is the *Bifilar pendulum*. Its period does not depend on the mass of the bar.

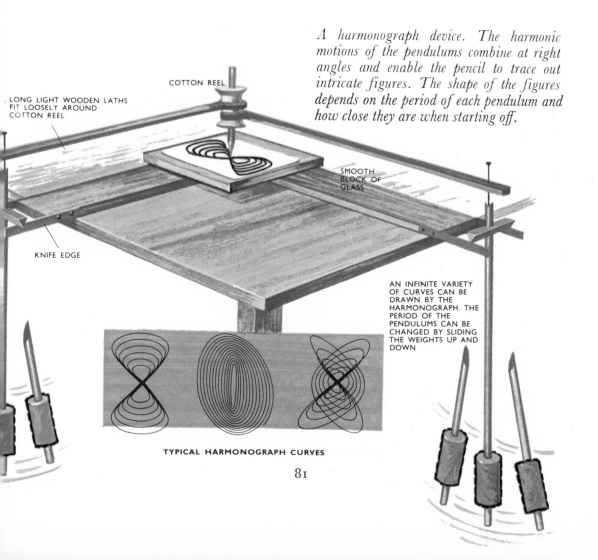

A harmonograph device. The harmonic motions of the pendulums combine at right angles and enable the pencil to trace out intricate figures. The shape of the figures depends on the period of each pendulum and how close they are when starting off.

COTTON REEL

LONG LIGHT WOODEN LATHS FIT LOOSELY AROUND COTTON REEL

SMOOTH BLOCK OF GLASS

KNIFE EDGE

AN INFINITE VARIETY OF CURVES CAN BE DRAWN BY THE HARMONOGRAPH. THE PERIOD OF THE PENDULUMS CAN BE CHANGED BY SLIDING THE WEIGHTS UP AND DOWN

TYPICAL HARMONOGRAPH CURVES

81

CHAPTER TWENTY-SEVEN

Zero 'g'

THE bigger the masses of objects the greater their gravitational pull on each other. In fact the gravitational pull of two bodies on each other is proportional to the *product* of their individual masses. The Earth is a huge object, with a mass of

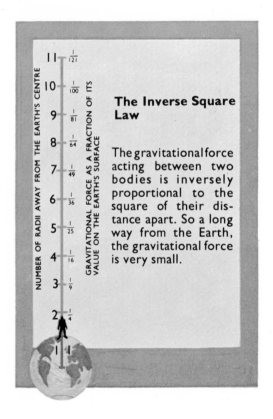

The Inverse Square Law

The gravitational force acting between two bodies is inversely proportional to the square of their distance apart. So a long way from the Earth, the gravitational force is very small.

about 5,883,000,000,000,000,000,000 tons, so quite naturally it exerts a fairly large gravitational force. The force was large enough to accelerate Newton's apple towards the Earth at 32 feet per second per second.

But the Earth's gravitational pull on an apple also depends on the distance of the apple from the Earth's centre of gravity. When it is on or near the surface of the Earth, the apple is roughly 4,000 miles from its centre. If the apple were dropped from a height twice the distance from the Earth's centre (8,000 miles from the centre, or 4,000 miles from the surface), then it would accelerate towards the Earth at a rate of only 8 feet per second per second. By doubling the distance away from the Earth's centre of gravity, the force of gravity has been reduced to a quarter of its value at the Earth's surface. Expressed mathematically, the force of gravity varies *inversely* as the *square of the distance apart of the two masses*.

So as the apple is taken farther and farther away from the Earth, the pull of the Earth's gravity on it becomes smaller and smaller. It can never become absolutely nothing, for then the apple would have to be an infinite distance away from the Earth. However, when the apple is a few thousands of miles away from the Earth, the effect of the Earth's gravity is very small. If the apple were released there it would fall towards the Earth, but would start to move extremely slowly.

This is very nearly the condition known as 'zero g' (zero gravity), and it is one of the many difficulties encountered by astronauts. It is surprising how much we rely on the pull of gravity to do everyday things. Even when pouring coffee into a cup, we put the coffee pot above the cup,

In this aircraft cabin, diving down in a curved path towards the Earth, the effect of the Earth's gravity is cancelled out. Zero g conditions can be held for only twenty seconds.

and let gravity pull the liquid down into the cup. If the astronaut were to try and do this in *zero g* conditions, the coffee would just float around in globules inside the space ship.

Moving would also be rather different for there would be no force of gravity to pull the astronaut back towards the floor. So if he thrust up-wards by pushing with his feet, he would continue to move upwards until he hit the ceiling.

Gravity and Acceleration

Astronauts would experience zero g when they were stationary in space, well away from the gravitational attractions of the Sun or any of the planets. They would also experience zero g when they were moving with

The lorry stops, but the crates continue moving forwards. Because the crates are not fixed to the lorry, they are not decelerated. When the lorry accelerates, the loose crates are left behind. As the space-ship accelerates things which are not fixed inside are similarly left.

83

On Earth, gravity pulls the liquid down into the glass. But under Zero g conditions, there is no such force.

constant velocity. But as soon as the space-ship starts to accelerate it gets back a 'force' which could easily be mistaken for the force of gravity.

Gravity and acceleration are closely connected things. As the force of gravity accelerated the apple so accelerating creates a 'force' very similar to the force of gravity.

As long as the space-ship is neither accelerating nor slowing down – in other words, it is either stationary or moving with constant velocity – its motion creates no gravity-like force. This ties in with Newton's First Law of Motion – 'If there are no forces acting on a body then nothing changes. If it is at rest, it stays at rest. If it is moving

with a certain velocity, then it continues to move in a straight line with that same velocity.' Now, in space, the converse of this law happens. In this instance the space-ship is either stationary or moving with constant velocity, so there are no forces.

Newton's second law of motion deals with the effect of a force on the motion of a body. 'Forces always produce accelerations, and an acceleration is proportional to the force producing it.' Again, the converse is true in the accelerating space-ship. *An acceleration produces a 'force'.*

If the space-ship accelerates at 32 feet per second per second, it would seem, to the astronaut, exactly like being on Earth. The 'force' produced by the movement would be indistinguishable from the downwards force of the Earth's gravity, because this also tends to accelerate objects at 32 feet per second per second.

For instance, if the space-ship started to accelerate from rest at the instant the astronaut started to pour his coffee, then the astronaut would think things were quite normal. There would be a definite 'up' direction and a definite 'down' direction, just as there is on the Earth. 'Up' in the space-ship would be in the direction of the nose and 'down' would be in the direction of the tail of the craft. The space-ship's floor would be the end nearest the tail, and, if the astronaut stood on it to pour his cup of coffee, the coffee would appear to drop into the cup.

However, although the astronaut would think things were Earth-like, they would appear subtly different to an impartial observer outside the space-ship. Suppose one astronaut were left behind in space while the ship was stationary, and he could see what happens as the space-ship accelerates away from him. Then, as soon as the coffee is poured, it is separated from the rest of the space-ship. The coffee is not accelerated forwards along with all the rest of the fixtures (including the coffee-pot) because it is not connected to anything. So no force acts on the coffee and it stays *exactly where it was when the space-ship was stationary.*

In fact, the space-ship, in accelerating forwards, catches up the coffee. The space-ship moves towards the coffee, but an astronaut in the space-ship, because he is accelerating forwards with the space-ship, cannot tell the difference between the space-ship's movement towards the coffee, and the thing he is used to on Earth, the coffee's downwards movement towards the Earth. There is nothing wrong with the perception of the astronaut, for there is absolutely no way of telling the difference.

To the stationary spaceman, the hammer stays still and the spaceman accelerates upwards. But the spaceman in the space-ship thinks the opposite. He thinks he has got back the force of gravity.

HAMMER STAYS STILL

HAMMER STAYS STILL

85

CHAPTER TWENTY-EIGHT

Gyroscopes

ANY cyclist knows that it is far easier to keep balance on a bicycle which is travelling fast than on one which is moving slowly. A spinning top will remain upright provided that its speed of rotation is high, but as it slows down it will topple over. In both these examples objects which are unstable (*i.e.* fall over easily) when they are stationary, can be made to remain erect provided that they are moving with sufficient speed.

This property of a wheel to continue to rotate in one plane in space once it has been set in motion is utilized in the gyrocompass, and in various other navigational aids both at sea and in the air. This behaviour is displayed particularly by wheels which have much of their weight near the rim. All such heavy wheels are called *gyroscopes*.

A gyroscopic wheel continues to spin in the same plane provided that no forces are applied in an attempt to change its direction of rotation. In a gyrocompass the wheel is mounted in such a way that any change in the position of its supports will not be transmitted to the wheel itself. Circular pivoted frameworks called *gimbals* are used for this purpose.

However, the wheel acts in a strange way if a turning force is applied to it. This effect may be demonstrated with a bicycle wheel which has been taken out of the frame. The two ends of the spindle are supported in the hands and the wheel is set spinning in the

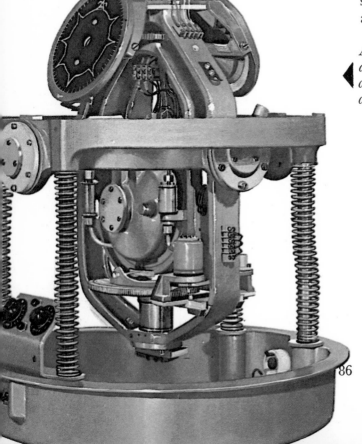

A modern gyrocompass which incorporates a mercury tube to ensure that it will indicate true North. Corrections are applied for changes in speed and latitude.

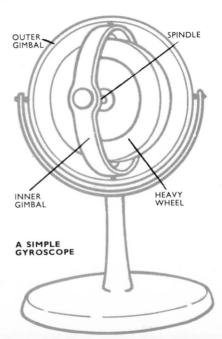

OUTER GIMBAL

SPINDLE

INNER GIMBAL

HEAVY WHEEL

A SIMPLE GYROSCOPE

vertical plane (*i.e.* the spindle is horizontal). Any attempt to turn the spindle in the horizontal plane is resisted but may eventually result in it being turned in a vertical plane at right angles to the vertical plane in which the wheel was spinning originally. This effect, which is known as *precession*, is felt by the hands. If the wheel is rotating fast it is quite difficult to maintain a grip on the spindle.

At one time the ability of a freely pivoted heavy wheel to continue to rotate in one plane in space was regarded only as a novelty and incorporated in various 'scientific' toys. But later the possibility of using a gyroscope as a direction indicator was realized. A gyrocompass is unaffected by magnetic fields (once it has been set, its axis stays pointing to true North, not magnetic North). This is its great advantage over magnetic compasses in ships at sea. With magnetic compasses corrections have to be applied for the local magnetic fields set up in the steel of the ship.

The behaviour of the wheel of a gyrocompass can best be demonstrated by subjecting a gyroscope to various turning forces such as may be exper-

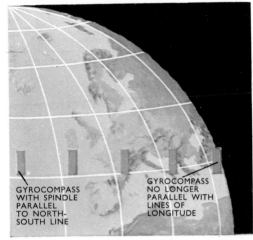

GYROCOMPASS WITH SPINDLE PARALLEL TO NORTH-SOUTH LINE

GYROCOMPASS NO LONGER PARALLEL WITH LINES OF LONGITUDE

If it goes uncorrected, the gyrocompass develops an Easterly variation in the Northern Hemisphere. Once it is spinning in a plane, the wheel remains parallel to that plane.

ienced in a ship at sea. As will be seen from the illustrations, the wheel of the gyroscope is freely pivoted inside one gimbal which is itself mounted in a second gimbal. By this means the gyroscope is free to rotate in any plane in space. In order that the wheel may continue to spin for as long as possible the bearings in which the spindles rotate have to be carefully designed to reduce friction as far as possible.

If such a gyroscope is placed on a

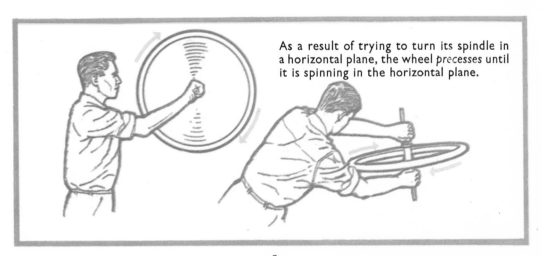

As a result of trying to turn its spindle in a horizontal plane, the wheel *precesses* until it is spinning in the horizontal plane.

It is much easier to keep balance on a bicycle which is going fast than one which is travelling more slowly.

table and is set spinning so that the axis of the wheel lies in an East-West direction (*i.e.* the wheel lies in the North-South plane), any attempt to tip the table about the North-South line will be resisted. The faster the wheel is rotating and the greater its mass the more difficult it will be to tip the table. However, if the table *is* tipped, the gyroscope will precess about its vertical axis until the spindle is parallel with the North-South line about which the table has been tipped. Thus the *spindle* of the gyroscope eventually *precesses* until it is *parallel* with the line about which the gyroscope was turned. Slight vibrations and movements received by the base of the gyroscope are not transferred to the wheel.

Even if a gyroscope is set up on an apparently firm table and set spinning with the spindle in an East-West line, the gyroscope will very slowly precess until the spindle lies in the North-South line. It may take several hours for the change to come about, so that to follow the movement it may be necessary to observe a mark on one of the gimbals through a miscroscope. This movement is caused as a result

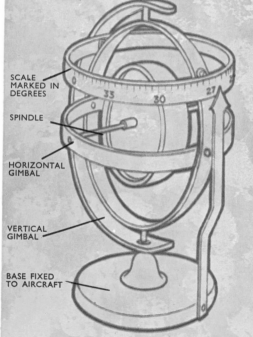

SCALE MARKED IN DEGREES

33 30 27

SPINDLE

HORIZONTAL GIMBAL

VERTICAL GIMBAL

BASE FIXED TO AIRCRAFT

Gyroscopic Aircraft Direction Indicator

As shown in the diagram this instrument is a specially modified gyroscope, and it is intended that the spindle of the heavy wheel shall remain horizontal. Since there is the minimum of friction at the gimbal mountings, once the gyroscope is rotating it will continue to spin in the same plane in space irrespective of the movement of the base.

Any change in the direction of motion of the aircraft will be indicated by a movement of the outermost (vertical) gimbal to which the scale (divided into degrees of arc) is attached. This scale moves relative to the pointer which is attached to the base of the instrument. As the aircraft changes direction, the base and pointer move with it while the scale and heavy wheel remain fixed in space.

of the rotation of the Earth about its axis (the line through true North and true South) and is the basis of the gyrocompass.

As frictional forces cannot be eliminated, it is necessary to supply energy to keep the wheel rotating, otherwise in time the wheel will stop. This energy can be supplied by means of an air jet impinging upon the edge of the rotor, or by making the 'wheel' the rotor of an electric motor.

In order that a gyroscope can be utilized as a direction finder various refinements are necessary. In particular it is found that once the gyroscope has been set rotating with its spindle pointing North, it tends in the Northern Hemisphere to move East. This is because the spindle tends to remain parallel to the original line about which the wheel was spinning, whereas the meridians or lines of longitude converge on the poles. As one end of the spindle tends to move East, it also tends to tilt upwards. To counteract this tendency the gyrocompass is fitted with cups of mercury at either end of its spindle. A narrow tube connects the cups so that when one end (East) of the spindle tilts upwards mercury flows from one cup to the other. The unbalancing effect of the flow of mercury causes the gyrocompass to *precess* until its spindle

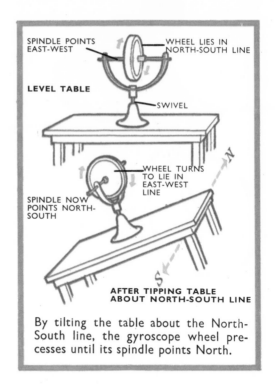

By tilting the table about the North-South line, the gyroscope wheel precesses until its spindle points North.

is again pointing North.

The principle of the gyroscope has been applied to the construction of various navigational aids and is particularly valuable in maintaining the course of torpedoes. By *rifling* (making spiral grooves in) the barrels of guns and rifles the projectiles are given a spin which reduces deviation from the intended path. In large ocean-going liners the stabilizing mechanism is controlled by a small gyroscope which detects the rolling motion.

RATE OF TURN INDICATOR

When an aircraft is being manoeuvred, one of the items of flight information that is required is the speed at which it is turning or changing its direction of flight. This information is especially important during 'blind flying', so that the direction in which the aircraft is pointing at a given time may be calculated. The actual speed or *rate* of turning is usually quite small in such cases. For example, an aircraft approaching an airport from the North may have to fly a few miles to the East of the airport before turning to make a landing into a westerly wind. In this case the

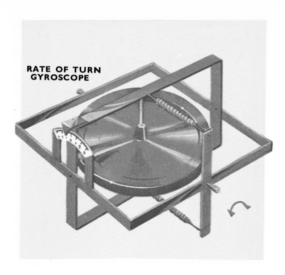

equal to the force which is causing the precession, the inner gymbal becomes stationary. The pointer attached to the inner gymbal indicates the position at which these forces equal each other, and this depends on the rate of turning in space of the outer gymbal. If the turning rate of the outer gymbal is increased the precession will increase. This will further stretch the spring until balance is again reached. On the other hand, if the turning rate of the outer gymbal is reduced the stretched spring will pull the inner gymbal back towards the zero turning rate position until balance is again reached. For zero rate of turn the springs will hold the inner gymbal at the 'zero' position.

aircraft will turn through an angle of 90° while flying at, say, 200 miles per hour. The time taken for this change of direction of flight from North-South to East-West might well take half a minute. The rate of turning would then be 90° in half a minute, or a turning rate of one complete revolution in two minutes.

Very low turning speeds of this sort are usually measured or indicated by means of a *rate of turn* or *angular velocity* gyroscope.

In this arrangement, when the outer gymbal is turned at a steady rate the flywheel precesses in the appropriate direction. As soon as precession begins and the inner gymbal starts to turn, one of the springs starts to stretch and so produces a force which opposes the precession. When the tension in the stretched spring is

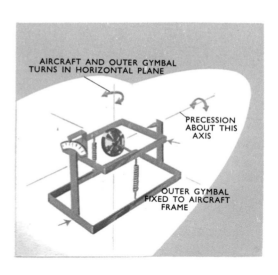

A rate of turn gyroscope (very much enlarged in proportion) in an aircraft.

Music and Noise

CHAPTER TWENTY-NINE

Vibration and Sound

EVERYTHING that makes a sound is vibrating and everything that vibrates makes a sound.

If you pluck a taut string it will vibrate and make a sound. The vibrating string pushes and pulls the surrounding air which, in turn, pushes and pulls the air beyond and in this way the vibrations are transmitted through the air to our ears as sound.

The vibrating string is like a moving vehicle; it compresses the air in front of it and creates a partial vacuum in the rear. But the air in front will not stay compressed for very long. It rapidly expands, and with such a force that it compresses the air in front. This in turn does

the same thing to the air beyond. In this way a wave of compressed air travels away from the string, rather like a rattling and banging noise runs along a line of stationary wagons when they are suddenly pushed by a locomotive (except that waves of compression travel outwards in *all* directions in the air).

The molecules of air do not have to travel very far in order to compress the air in front of them, so it is not the actual molecules of air that travel from the vibrating string to our ears, simply the waves of compression.

The actual sound waves (waves of compression) travel very quickly

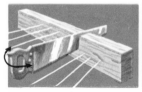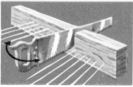

The pitch of the sound made by a vibrating saw depends on the rate at which it is vibrating. This in turn depends upon the length that is allowed to vibrate. The shorter the length the more frequent the vibrations and the higher the pitch of the sound.

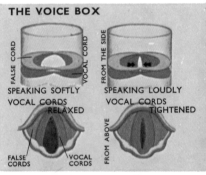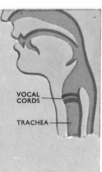

THE VOICE BOX

FALSE CORD · VOCAL CORD
FROM THE SIDE

SPEAKING SOFTLY
VOCAL CORDS RELAXED

FALSE CORDS · VOCAL CORDS
FROM ABOVE

SPEAKING LOUDLY
VOCAL CORDS TIGHTENED

The human voice results from air being passed over the vocal cords when we breathe out, causing them to vibrate. These vibrations are transmitted through the air and picked up by our ears as sound. The pitch of the sound is governed by the tautness of the cords, since this varies the rate at which they vibrate.

VOCAL CORDS

TRACHEA

Vibrations travel through SOLIDS
You can hear through a solid because it too transmits vibrations.

Vibrations travel through LIQUIDS
A liquid also transmits vibrations, making it possible to hear underwater, for instance.

... But NOT through a VACUUM
You cannot hear through a vacuum; there is nothing to carry the vibrations (sound) to your ears.

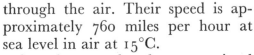

Vibrations travel through AIR
The vibrations of a bell are transmitted through the air and picked up by our ears as sound.

through the air. Their speed is approximately 760 miles per hour at sea level in air at 15°C.

Sound can also be transmitted through a liquid or a solid in the same manner as through air. Sound waves travel faster through solids and liquids than they do through gases. Their speed depends mainly upon the resistance of the substance to compression and the weight of its molecules. The heavier its molecules the greater the effort needed to move them, so the slower they will travel, while the more resistant they are to compression the faster they will·recover after being compressed. Iron, for instance, is much heavier than air but its resistance to compression is even greater and, on balance, sound waves travel almost fourteen times faster through iron than they do through air. A liquid is heavier than air, but, once again, it is much more resistant to compression. Sound waves travel faster in a liquid than in a gas but not as fast as they do in a solid. In water, for instance, they travel four times faster than in air. The one thing sound cannot

Moving in one direction (*left*) a vibrating string compresses the air in front of it and creates a partial vacuum in the rear. Moving in the opposite direction (*right*) it does exactly the same thing. The waves of compression are transmitted through the air away from the vibrating string (*below*).

be transmitted through is a vacuum. If the air is drawn out of a jar containing a suspended bell and the bell is 'rung' no sound can be heard from it. The bell is vibrating normally but there is no air for it to beat. In other words, there is no way of transmitting its vibrations to our ears.

As they travel outward from the source of vibration the waves of compression gradually die out. This is another way of saying the greater the distance the fainter the sound. What

happens is that the work done by molecules moving other molecules warms them up and in this way uses up the energy given them by the source of vibration. Another thing to be taken into account is that compression waves spread out in all directions so the initial energy given by the vibrating body must be used to move an ever increasing number of molecules of air.

The rate at which an object vibrates governs the 'pitch' or note of the sound it makes.

CHAPTER THIRTY

Musical Instruments and Pitch

THE great Italian scientist Galileo first put forward the idea that the pitch of a sound was determined by the frequency of its vibrations. This theory was verified by Hooke later in the 17th century. Hooke made a wheel which had small teeth sticking out from the edge at equal intervals all round it. He rotated the wheel on an axle and pressed a card onto the teeth so that a sound was given out by the teeth hitting against the card. A similar sound is given out when a ruler is dragged across some railings. If there were 100 teeth on the wheel and the wheel was rotating twice every second, then in one second the card would be hit 200 times by the teeth and the frequency of the sound would be 200 vibrations per second. By increasing the speed at which the wheel was rotated, the frequency would automatically be increased too. Hooke noticed that this increase in speed and frequency gave rise to notes of higher pitch. Incidentally, it can also be proved that the irregular frequencies of a wheel with unevenly spaced teeth do not give a note of a certain pitch but only an unmusical, unpleasant noise. More modern methods of producing notes of a given pitch work by

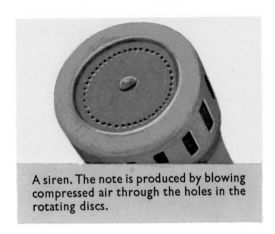

A siren. The note is produced by blowing compressed air through the holes in the rotating discs.

blowing compressed air through holes that are evenly spaced round the circumference of a rotating disc. The siren works on this principle.

When a jet of compressed air plays on a hole in the disc, the air can pass through the hole. When the solid part of the disc swings into position the jet of air is cut off. As the succession of holes appears in front of the jet, a succession of puffs of air are produced. These set up a train of sound waves.

The human mind is very expert at judging the relationship between a certain series of notes and even a slight mistake in pitch for one of them is displeasing to the ear. The relation-

When a large part of the ruler is vibrating the wavelength of the fundamental note produced is longer and the pitch is lower than when a small part is vibrating.

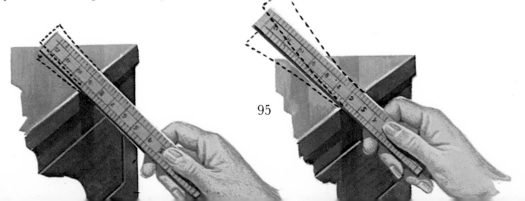

Left: *Drawing a bow across a violin string causes it to vibrate and shake the surrounding air.* Right: *With a trumpet or a bugle it is not the instrument that sets the air vibrating but the lips of the player.*

Left: *The flute player blows across a hole in the instrument and this causes the air to vibrate.* Right: *The air is caused to vibrate in instruments like the oboe when it strikes the sharp edge of a flexible reed.*

ships which are pleasing are arranged in a scale (doh, ray, me, fah, soh, lah, te, doh). Each of these notes has a different frequency and the relationship or ratios between them form the Diatonic Scale. If any series of notes is played in these ratios the result will be a scale, no matter which note (frequency) is taken as the starting point.

The diatonic scale runs into difficulties with the pianoforte, for, if it is made and tuned to give a perfect scale starting at, say, C as doh, the result is displeasing if we try to play the scale starting with D as doh. In order to play a true scale for every note there would have to be about 70 notes per octave, which would make the piano an impossible instrument to play. The compromise which has been adopted is the *tempered scale*, first suggested by the composer Johann Sebastian Bach (1685–1750). It is designed so that a scale can be played starting with any note, and although the ratios are never exactly right they are near enough to satisfy the musical ear.

Different musical instruments can obtain their variations in pitch by different methods. Although a ruler is not a musical instrument, it can be used to demonstrate how pitch can be made to vary. If it is held by one end and the table edge is banged with the other, it gives out a high pitched 'note'. Banging lower down the ruler, nearer to the hand, gives a lower pitched 'note'. For this low pitched 'note' the vibrating part of the ruler (between the table and the free end) is longer than when the high 'note' is being produced. In general the longer the vibrating part of the instrument, the lower the pitch becomes.

Whatever the pitch of the note the sound still travels at the same speed. The speed of sound is equal to the frequency of the note times its wavelength. $V = n\lambda$ where V is the speed of sound, n is the frequency and the Greek letter, λ is the wavelength. It stands to reason that if the speed of sound is to remain the same, high pitched notes (high frequency) will have small wave-lengths and low pitched notes (low frequency) will have large wave-lengths. A long string or rod fixed at both ends, or a long tube, will give a low note, whereas a short one will give a high note.

DIATONIC SCALE. When the frequencies of *doh, ray, me, fah, soh, lah, te, doh* are compared the following are the ratios:

doh	ray	me	fah	soh	lah	te	doh
1	9/8	5/4	4/3	3/2	5/3	15/8	2

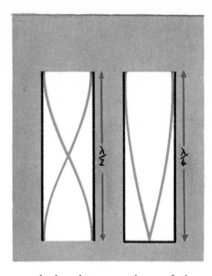

The double bass and the bassoon produce notes of lower pitch than the smaller violin and clarinet.

Open and closed organ pipes of the same length. The closed pipe produces the lower pitched note.

This is because the bigger rod or string cannot vibrate with as high a frequency as a smaller one.

One has only to look at the families of instruments in the orchestra to see that this is so. The double bass makes low pitched notes while the smaller violin makes high pitched notes. The bassoon makes lower pitched sounds than the clarinet.

The xylophone is a series of plates of different sizes connected together by two cords running near the ends of the plates. When struck, the centre of the plate vibrates and the ends

The pianoforte is a stringed instrument. The strings vibrate when struck with hammers tripped by the lever action of the keys, thus producing a musical note.

(which are nodes) do not. The vibration of the plates sets up sound waves in the air. The pitches of the notes produced depend on the frequency of vibration of the plates. The long plates give out the notes of low pitch. This is because a heavier and longer plate cannot vibrate with as high a frequency as a smaller one. With the guitar, the pitch can be raised by making the effective length of the string shorter by pressing it onto a stop on the finger board. Organ pipes are of two types, some which are open at both ends (open pipes) and others which are closed at one end (closed pipes). There is always an antinode at an open end and a node at a closed end. The basic, or *fundamental* sound produced in an open pipe has a wavelength of twice the effective length of the pipe. That produced by a closed pipe is four times its effective length. A closed pipe will produce a note of much lower pitch than an open pipe of the same length. The organ has many pipes because each of its pipes has a fixed pitch. Instruments such as the clarinet, though, can change pitch. Uncovering a certain hole in the pipe alters its effective length and changes the wavelength and pitch.

The pitch of a note produced by a wire does not entirely depend upon its length. It also depends upon how tightly it is stretched (the tension in the wire) and upon its 'heaviness' (linear density). The way in which tension affects pitch can be shown quite simply by plucking on a rubber band. The more the band is stretched, the higher is the pitch. Stringed instruments are tuned by adjusting the tension in their strings.

On stringed instruments, some strings are thin and light and others are thick and heavy. The light strings give notes of high pitch and the thick, heavy ones, deep notes of lower pitch. The effective (vibrating) length of each string must also be taken into account.

CHAPTER THIRTY-ONE

Resonance

EVERY object has a *natural* frequency of vibration. In other words, if an object is allowed to vibrate freely it will make a definite number of vibrations each second. An object can be *made* to vibrate at almost any rate we wish by applying forces to it at regular intervals (this is called forced vibration) but the amplitude (size) of the vibrations will be small. *Resonance* is the enormous increase in the size of the vibration that occurs when the frequency of the applied force happens to equal the natural frequency of the object.

A suspension bridge, for instance, has a natural frequency of vibration depending upon a number of factors such as its size, method of construction and the materials from which it is built. This is why a company of soldiers crossing such a bridge is ordered to break step; there is just a slight chance that the frequency of the marching steps might equal the natural (resonant) frequency of the bridge and cause vibration to build up to a dangerous extent. It has been

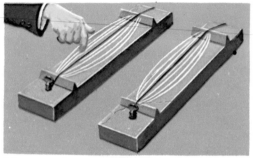

If two strings are tuned to the same note (i.e. tuned so their natural frequencies are the same), and one is plucked the other vibrates as well. The sound waves cause a sympathetic vibration.

known for wind to make an apparently sound bridge vibrate at its natural frequency and for swaying to build up until the whole structure has collapsed. In a similar way wine glasses can be shattered by the singing of high notes. Again the explanation is that the glass vibrated vigorously *in sympathy* with sounds whose frequencies are the same as the natural frequency of the glass. Waves of compressed air (sound waves) striking the glass at the same rate as its natural frequency cause resonance and the glass literally shakes itself to pieces.

A wind instrument's effective resonant length is changed by unstopping a hole.

ALL HOLES STOPPED. VIBRATIONS IN WHOLE LENGTH.

HOLE OPEN. VIBRATIONS CROWDED INTO SHORTER PIPE SO INCREASING THE FREQUENCY.

Musical instruments depend upon the fact that every stretched string, every pipe, diaphragm or reed has its own natural vibration frequency. When set in motion each will send out vibrations of its own frequency into the surrounding air. If a guitar string is kept at a constant tension it will vibrate at the same rate every time it is plucked. In other words, the note produced will always be the same, since the pitch of the sound depends upon the frequency of vibration. An organ pipe will always produce the same note too. When a jet of air strikes the sharp edge of the pipe it vibrates at many different frequencies but only one of these, equal to the natural frequency of the pipe, will cause the air in the pipe to vibrate any considerable amount and produce a loud note, i.e. will cause resonance.

The natural (or resonant) frequency of a pipe can be altered if the length of the vibrating column of air in the pipe is changed. In other words the pitch of the sound or note it produces can be altered in this way. The shorter the length of the air that is allowed to vibrate the higher the frequency of vibration and hence the higher the note. The longer the length that is allowed to vibrate the lower the frequency and the lower the note. The slide of a trombone, for instance, alters the resonant length of the pipe, i.e. the length of the column of air that is allowed to vibrate (in sympathy with *one* of the many forced vibrations set up by players' lips) and thus alters the note it is heard to play.

CHAPTER THIRTY-TWO

Nodes and Antinodes

WHEN a tuning fork is struck, the prongs are set into motion, back and forth, and the prongs set up vibrations in the surrounding air molecules. The air molecules follow a form of motion very similar to the prong itself – as the prong moves outwards a thin layer of air molecules is pushed outwards with it. The molecules in the layer then not only return to their original positions, but move beyond (like a pendulum bob). But before they do so, they push out the molecules in the adjoining air layer. These molecules then swing out and return to their original positions and through the other side and back again. In the process, they set the *next* layer vibrating. In this manner, the vibration of the prong of the fork is copied by vibrations in successive layers of air. The vibrations travel outwards from the fork. It should be remembered that it is only the *vibrations* of air that are being sent out from the fork; there is no transfer of the air itself.

This is a form of *longitudinal* wave – the vibrations occur in a direction *along* the direction of motion of travel of the sound. The *rate* at which vibration 'bundles' are sent out from the fork depends on the frequency of vibration of the prongs – this determines the *pitch* of the sound that is heard. The distance between each vibration bundle is the *wavelength* of the sound.

Sound is emitted in this form, as a moving pattern of vibration waves. But in many musical instruments – an organ pipe, for example, there are *stationary* patterns of waves set up. An organ pipe is stimulated into giving out a musical note when air is blown into its end. A regular pattern of vibrating layers of air molecules is

set up in the pipe.

In the pipe, a region of vibrating layers of molecules merges into a region of no vibration. This merges into another region of vibrating molecules. The regions of maximum vibration are called *anti nodes*, those of no vibration, *nodes*. In a closed pipe it is obvious that a node must exist at the closed end – the molecules cannot possibly vibrate against a fixed surface. The antinode exists at the open end.

The stationary wave (or *standing wave pattern*) is formed when a sound wave travels down the tube and is reflected at the closed end. The two waves, forward (*incident*) and *reflected*, 'mix' together and interfere. At the nodes, the two waves always cancel each other out, but at the antinodes the waves add to each other, so the nodes represent a position of no vibration, but the antinodes repre-

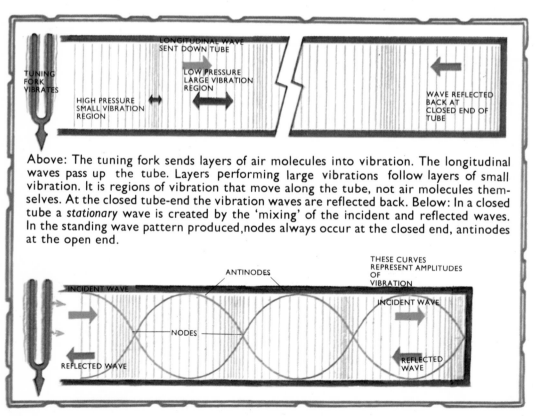

Above: The tuning fork sends layers of air molecules into vibration. The longitudinal waves pass up the tube. Layers performing large vibrations follow layers of small vibration. It is regions of vibration that move along the tube, not air molecules themselves. At the closed tube-end the vibration waves are reflected back. Below: In a closed tube a *stationary* wave is created by the 'mixing' of the incident and reflected waves. In the standing wave pattern produced, nodes always occur at the closed end, antinodes at the open end.

In Kundt's tube the positions of the nodes are shown where the small piles of lycopodium powder collect. Stroking the rod makes the attached plate vibrate and the standing wave pattern is produced in the tube. The distances between the nodes is one-half of a wavelength of the sound.

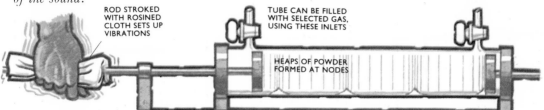

ROD STROKED WITH ROSINED CLOTH SETS UP VIBRATIONS

TUBE CAN BE FILLED WITH SELECTED GAS, USING THESE INLETS

HEAPS OF POWDER FORMED AT NODES

sent a position of maximum vibration, of air molecules.

The existence of nodes and anti-nodes can be demonstrated in a number of different ways. The best-known demonstration is in *Kundt's tube*. A long clamped rod is attached to a flat plate within a glass tube, which is set into vibration when the rod is stroked with a resined cloth. The plate sends out sound vibrations into a long glass tube. Into the tube is sprinkled fine lycopodium powder or sand. The rod is moved into the tube so that the sound waves it gives out 'fit' the tube – an antinode is at the open end when there is the node at the closed end. (The tube is then said to *resonate*.) At antinodes the vibration of the air 'sweeps' the powder away and it accumulates at positions of no vibration – the nodes. The resulting regularly-arranged piles of powder along the tube represent the position of the nodes.

CHAPTER THIRTY-THREE

Harmonics

MUSIC would be unimaginably dull if all musical instruments playing a certain note—say middle C—were to sound exactly alike. A trumpet and a violin would produce indistinguishable sounds and there would be no point in making different musical instruments. Both of these instruments are capable of producing the same note and yet sounding quite different. They make the air around them vibrate with a certain frequency. In the case of middle C, this is at 256 vibrations per second. The basic vibration with the largest possible wave size is called the *fundamental*. The best known instrument capable of producing the funda-mental without producing additional waves is the tuning fork (which is used for tuning pianos) and because of this gives out a very 'tinny' note. *Additional* sound waves give the 'body' or quality to musical notes. These additional sound waves are called *harmonics*. When a note is played, fundamental vibrations are set up and also other vibrations (called harmonics or over-tones). A vibration with a wave half as long as the fundamental is called the 2nd harmonic; a vibration with a wave one-third as long is called the 3rd harmonic and so on. The different sound qualities of instruments depend on the fact that together with the

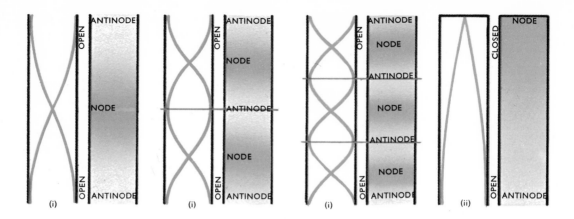

fundamental, or first harmonic, certain other harmonics are played, some more loudly than others.

Pictures of the wave forms of sounds can be obtained by using an electronic apparatus called the cathode ray oscilloscope. It gives a still picture of wave forms that really are repeating hundreds or thousands of times a second. The picture will be of a very complicated wave which is a combination of the fundamental and various harmonics and will need

to be unscrambled by a mechanical harmonic analyser into simple waves, one representing each harmonic. The harmonics of some waves are so faint that they can be ignored. In the case of a clarinet, playing the note G above middle C, the 1st and 3rd harmonics are the most important, the 4th and 5th are of lesser importance. The second harmonic is almost undetectable.

Two different types of organ pipes playing the same note produce different sounds due to the presence of different harmonics or overtones. The two types of organ pipes are the open organ pipe which has both ends open and produces antinodes

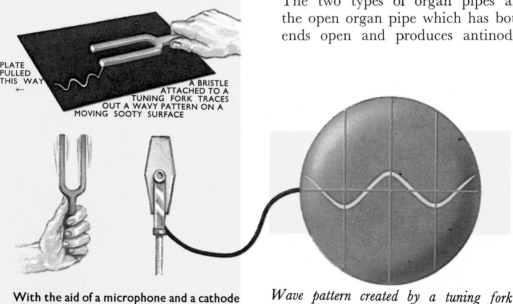

With the aid of a microphone and a cathode ray oscillograph, wave can be made visible.

Wave pattern created by a tuning fork sounding the G note above middle C.

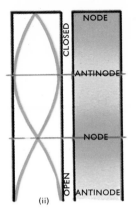 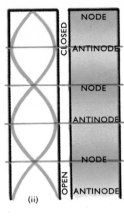

(ii) (ii)

(Left) *Open organ pipes* (i) *always have antinodes* (*where the air molecules vibrate most vigorously*) *at their open ends and can make all the possible harmonics* (*second, third, fourth, etc.*), *whereas closed ones* (ii) *which must have nodes* (*where the air molecules are at rest*) *at their closed ends can only give odd-numbered harmonics* (*3rd, 5th, etc.*).

The waves show how the complicated wave pattern of the G note of the clarinet is built up by combining the fundamental with its various harmonics. The shape of the final pattern is largely determined here by the addition of the fundamental and 3rd harmonics (the 2nd harmonic is absent). The 4th and 5th harmonics only slightly alter the wave shape.

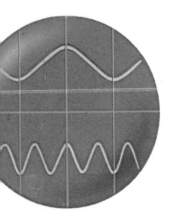 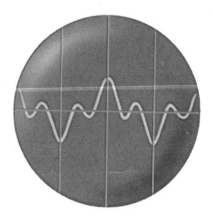 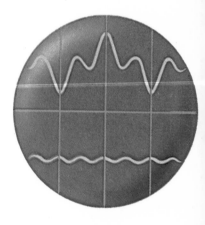

(1) Wave shapes of fundamental and 3rd harmonics.

(2) First resultant obtained by adding the 3rd harmonic to the fundamental.

(3) First resultant and wave pattern of 4th harmonic.

(4) Second resultant obtained by adding first resultant and 4th harmonic.

(5) Second resultant and 5th harmonic.

(6) Third resultant obtained by adding 5th harmonic to second resultant.

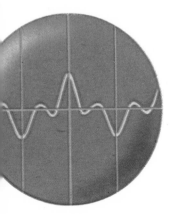 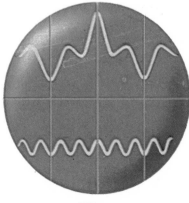 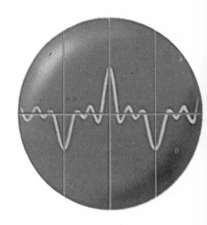

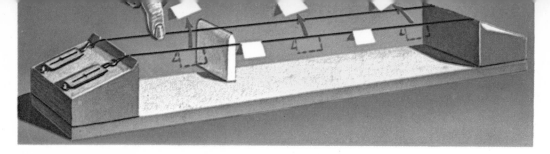

This sonometer has two identical wires. A bridge is placed one third the way along the back wire thereby stopping the wire from moving and forming a node. The shorter section of this wire is plucked in the middle. The front wire vibrates in sympathy. Pieces of paper jump off this wire at antinodes (maximum vibration) and stay on at nodes (no vibration).

(places where vibrations are largest) at each end, and the closed organ pipe which produces an antinode at the open end and a node (place of no vibration) at the closed end.

Diagram (i) shows how the air in an open organ pipe can vibrate in a number of ways, in each case keeping an antinode at each end. The simplest method of vibration occurs when

there is just one node, half way along the pipe. The sound produced by this vibration is the fundamental or first harmonic. At the same time the air in the pipe can vibrate so that there are two nodes, one-quarter and three-quarters the way along the pipe. This gives rise to the second harmonic—a sound whose wavelength is half that of the fundamental. The same pipe can also produce 3rd, 4th and 5th and higher harmonics.

Diagram (ii) shows how the air in an organ pipe closed at one end can vibrate in a number of ways, in each case keeping a node at the closed end and an antinode at the open end. With just one node and one antinode the pipe sounds its fundamental note or first harmonic. With a second node one-third of the way up the pipe the sound produced has a wavelength of one-third that of the fundamental. This gives rise to the *third* harmonic. A closed pipe has no second harmonic—it has only odd-numbered harmonics. Because it lacks even-numbered harmonics the closed organ pipe gives a sound of different quality from the open-ended pipe, though their fundamental notes may be the same.

Harmonics or overtones are what makes the violin sound different from the euphonium. They give the notes their distinctive quality.

FUNDAMENTAL
(FIRST HARMONIC)

SECOND
HARMONIC

THIRD
HARMONIC

FOURTH
HARMONIC

FIFTH
HARMONIC

A sonometer. The top wire is sounding its fundamental note, the others are sounding their 2nd, 3rd, 4th and 5th harmonics.

CHAPTER THIRTY-FOUR

The Ear

THE human ear is a delicate organ, parts of which control the body's sense of balance and parts of which are concerned with receiving sound signals before they are passed as impulses along a nerve to the brain.

Sound waves are collected by the outer ear which is bounded on the outside by a flap of skin (the ear lobe that we see) called the *pinna* and on the inside by a taut membrane, the *ear drum*.

Sound waves make the ear drum vibrate in sympathy. This movement of the ear drum is conveyed through the *middle ear* (a cavity which contains air) by three tiny bones to the *oval window* which is at the innermost side of the middle ear. Beyond the oval window is the *inner ear*. The part of the inner ear which is concerned with hearing is called the *cochlea*, a coiled horn-like tube filled with fluid. Vibrations of the oval window produce pressure changes on the fluid in the cochlea which affect tiny, sensitive hairs that link up with nerve fibre. The movement of these hairs results in impulses being sent along the nerve fibres which join to form the auditory nerve and which carry the impulses to the brain.

In the brain these impulses are translated as sound. The ear does not

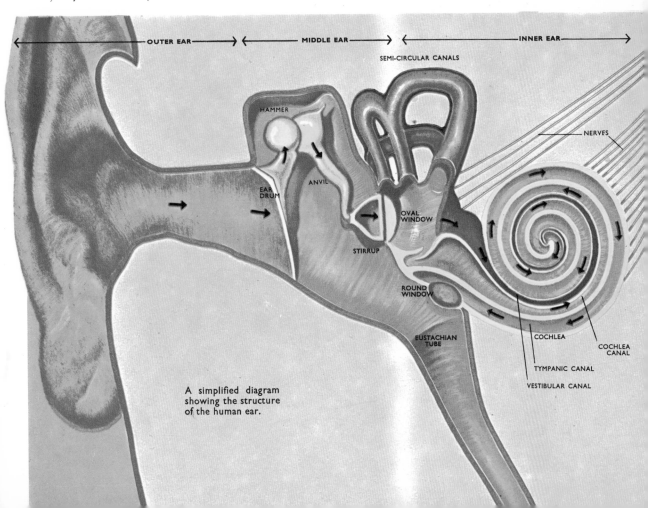

OUTER EAR ———→ ←——— MIDDLE EAR ———→ ← ———————————— INNER EAR ————————————→

SEMI-CIRCULAR CANALS

HAMMER

NERVES

EAR DRUM

ANVIL

OVAL WINDOW

STIRRUP

ROUND WINDOW

EUSTACHIAN TUBE

COCHLEA

COCHLEA CANAL

TYMPANIC CANAL

VESTIBULAR CANAL

A simplified diagram showing the structure of the human ear.

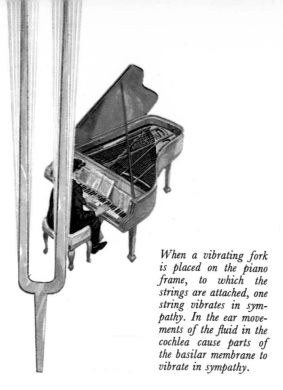

When a vibrating fork is placed on the piano frame, to which the strings are attached, one string vibrates in sympathy. In the ear movements of the fluid in the cochlea cause parts of the basilar membrane to vibrate in sympathy.

hear—it merely receives sound waves which are transmitted as impulses to the brain. It is the brain which interprets these as sound.

The middle ear is connected to the back of the throat by a narrow tube —the *eustachian tube*. This is normally closed by a small muscle but when we swallow or cough the tube opens to admit air to the middle ear from the throat. This ensures that the pressure in the middle ear is the same as that in the outer ear (i.e. equal pressures are maintained in either side of the ear drum).

The area of the ear drum or *tympanic membrane* (about $\frac{1}{7}$ square inch) is nearly thirty times that of the oval window (about $\frac{1}{200}$ square inch) and the ear bones form a system of levers which 'gear down' the movements of the tympanic membrane. This size difference between the two membranes and the 'gearing down' result in the pressure on the oval window being twenty-two times that of the original pressure of the vibration on the tympanic membrane.

The ear is protected from very loud sounds by the action of two muscles —one attached to the tympanic membrane and the other to the *stirrup*. When these shorten, the tympanic membrane and the oval window (to which the stirrup is attached) become more taut so that the extent of their to-and-fro movement is reduced.

The wall of the cochlea is a rigid substance, bone, and since the cochlea is filled with fluid (and fluids cannot be compressed) the to-and-fro movements of the oval window cause pressure changes on the fluid. These pressure changes cause the *basilar membrane*, to which the sensitive hair cells are attached, to vibrate in unison. The accompanying stimulation of the hairs on the hair cells results in impulses passing along the ear nerve of the brain.

The cochlea, if it is straightened out, can be seen to be a tapered tube containing three fluid-filled canals, the two outer of which are in communication with each other at the apex of the cochlea through a small opening. The oval window closes the end of one of these canals (the *vestibular canal*) while another membrane, the round window, closes the other (the *tympanic canal*). When the oval window bulges inwards (i.e. is pushed by the stapes) the pressure change in the fluid in the canals causes the round window to bulge outwards. This is probably a safety device which provides pressure relief.

The ear receives a musical note as a sound wave and the brain, from the information it receives by way of nervous impulses, is able to determine the pitch, loudness and quality of the note.

It is thought that the 'judgment' of pitch is, at least in part, due to the

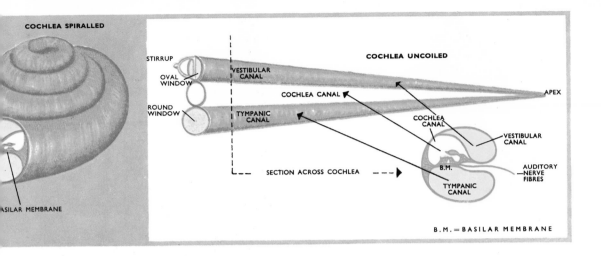

COCHLEA SPIRALLED

STIRRUP

OVAL
WINDOW

ROUND
WINDOW

VESTIBULAR
CANAL

TYMPANIC
CANAL

COCHLEA UNCOILED

COCHLEA CANAL

APEX

SECTION ACROSS COCHLEA

COCHLEA
CANAL

VESTIBULAR
CANAL

B.M.

TYMPANIC
CANAL

AUDITORY
—NERVE
FIBRES

BASILAR MEMBRANE

B.M. = BASILAR MEMBRANE

structure of the basilar membrane. This contains many fibres which are arranged at right-angles to the length of the cochlea. Fibres at the base of the cochlea are shorter than those at its apex and when different sounds are received by the ear different parts of the basilar membrane vibrate to a greater extent than other parts. Low frequency sounds cause the fibres at the upper end of the basilar membrane to vibrate, while higher frequency sounds cause the fibres nearer the base of the membrane to vibrate.

CHAPTER THIRTY-FIVE

The Microphone

THE sound of a voice is the vibration of vocal cords in the speaker's throat. The vibration of the cords is transmitted through the surrounding air, picked up by our ears and interpreted by our brain as sound. It is common knowledge that sound dies away with distance. In other words, the vibrations or sound waves die down slowly as they travel through the air. But there are many instances where it is necessary to take the sound of a voice further than it would carry normally. Take, for example, the case of a public address system in a large building with numerous rooms whose walls would prevent sound travelling directly, or that of a person wishing to speak to somebody in a distant town. This can be done with the aid of an electrical circuit containing a microphone.

The function of a microphone is to set up electric currents which vary in strength exactly in time with vibrations in the surrounding air. In other words, it makes an electrical reproduction of sound waves. Although there are several kinds of microphone, all contain a disc, or *diaphragm*, which vibrates in sympathy with sound waves striking it. When a person speaks into a microphone the vibrations of his voice strike the diaphragm and cause it to vibrate in sympathy (i.e. to vibrate with exactly the same rhythm). The vibrating diaphragm then either sets up or modifies an electric current which varies in strength in time with its own vibration and, hence, with the vibration of the speaker's voice.

The next step is to convey the electrical reproduction of the sound waves to the place where they need to be heard and turn it back into actual vibrations which can be picked up by the ear as sounds. The instrument which does this (a loud-speaker) works on the reverse principle to the microphone; the varying electric current entering it is made to vibrate a diaphragm and the vibrations of the diaphragm travel out through the air as sound waves. In between the microphone and the loud-speaker the current strength is usually magnified (without altering its rhythm) by means

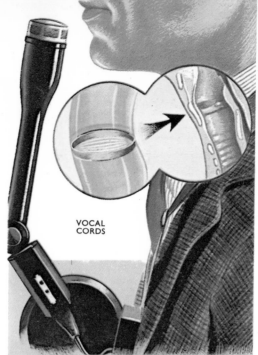

VOCAL CORDS

The sound of a voice is the vibration of vocal cords in the speaker's throat (see inset).

Types of Microphone

In the moving-coil microphone a diaphragm is attached to a light coil of wire between the poles of a permanent magnet. As the diaphragm vibrates in sympathy with the speaker's voice the coil moves with it. When a wire is moved near the end of a magnet an electric current is produced (always providing that there is a complete circuit for the current to flow through) and the to-and-fro vibration movement sets up a to-and-fro electric current in step with it. Thus the moving coil sets up an electric current which varies in time and strength with the vibrations of the diaphragm and hence with the vibrations of the speaker's voice. A very sensitive modern microphone is the crystal type. Its diaphragm is fixed to a slice of material, such as quartz, which becomes electrically charged when compressed. The size of the charge varies in time with the vibrations of the diaphragm. Yet another type in common use is the condenser microphone. This contains a condenser, a device for holding static electricity. One plate of the condenser forms the diaphragm, and the capacity of the condenser varies in time with the vibrations of the diaphragm.

of amplifying valves. The increased current strength makes the diaphragm in the loud-speaker vibrate more strongly than the diaphragm in the microphone but still in time with the microphone vibrations.

There are various ways of making electrical reproductions of sound waves. The diaphragm in the mouthpiece of a telephone carries a small flat disc of graphite (a form of carbon). Sandwiched between this and a similar disc fixed nearby are a number of fragments of graphite, loosely packed. As the vibrations of the speaker's voice strike the diaphragm it vibrates in sympathy and the first

disc vibrates with it (but not the second). Thus the loose graphite 'filling' of the 'sandwich' is alternately compressed and released. The electrical resistance of the 'sandwich' depends upon how tightly the graphite fragments are pushed down. Since this varies with the vibration of the diaphragm, so does the electrical resistance. Thus a current passed through the microphone from a battery will vary in strength in time with the vibrations of the diaphragm too. These electrical reproductions are conveyed through wires to a distant listener and converted back into real sound waves in the earpiece of his telephone.

The Telephone

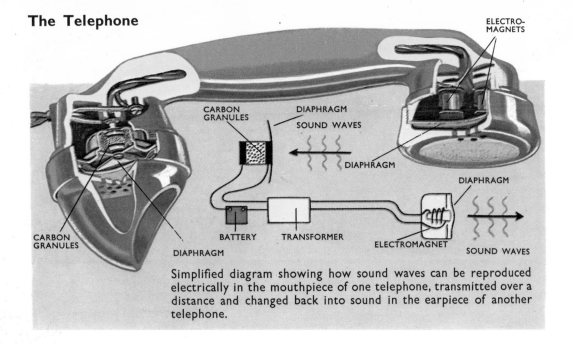

CARBON GRANULES
DIAPHRAGM
SOUND WAVES
ELECTRO-MAGNETS
DIAPHRAGM
CARBON GRANULES
DIAPHRAGM
BATTERY
TRANSFORMER
ELECTROMAGNET
DIAPHRAGM
SOUND WAVES

Simplified diagram showing how sound waves can be reproduced electrically in the mouthpiece of one telephone, transmitted over a distance and changed back into sound in the earpiece of another telephone.

CHAPTER THIRTY-SIX

The Acoustics of Buildings

IN designing a concert hall or theatre, the architect not only has to take into account the number of people to be seated and the arrangement of the seats in relation to one another, the position of the gangways and exit doors and details of ventilation and illumination. He must also give careful consideration to the acoustics of the building. Will the full range of sound waves reach every seat in the auditorium? Will there be too much reflection, or is too much sound going to be absorbed by the walls and ceiling?

Sound waves travel in straight lines and will go out from their source in all directions. In much the same way as with light, sound waves can be reflected or absorbed by surfaces which they strike. Thus hard polished surfaces reflect sound, while softer matt surfaces absorb it.

A concave surface tends to focus sound waves over a small area.

As the sound absorption properties of a particular substance vary for different frequencies, it is desirable that sound should have an unobstructed path from the source on the platform direct to each member of the audience. For this reason pillars and other obstacles in the auditorium are to be avoided if at all possible. Modern methods of construction, especially the use of pre-stressed concrete, are valuable in this respect.

The final tonal quality of the sound depends largely upon a portion of the sound waves reaching the listener by reflection. Each time a sound wave is reflected, some of the sound is lost by absorption. Thus after it has been reflected a few times, the sound will die away completely. There will always be a slight time

109

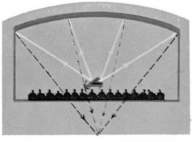

Sound waves which may otherwise be lost are deflected into the auditorium by reflectors behind the source.

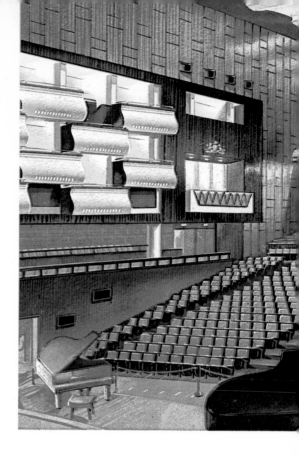

The curved roof of a concert hall reflects sound over a large area of the auditorium.

lag during which the sound gradually dies away even if the source is stopped suddenly. This time lag is known as the *reverberation time* and a satisfactory value for concert halls of moderate size is about 2 seconds.

The extent of the reflections will depend partly upon the shape and size of the auditorium, but also upon the nature and relative proportions of the reflecting and absorbing surfaces. Irregularities in the walls and ceilings, in the form of alcoves and recesses, can cause unwanted reflections and are to be avoided. The height of the roof of the concert hall and the curvature of its surface have to be carefully chosen in order that the sound waves which it collects are reflected back over as large an area of the auditorium as possible. Otherwise there is a risk of there being 'dead' spots where reflected sound cancels out direct sound.

At the design stage the wise architect will check the acoustic properties of a proposed concert hall, either by means of models or by calculations based on the rules for reflection of sound. One method of testing models is to make lengthwise sections of the hall and to place them in a shallow tank of water. Vibrations are then set up in the water from the point corresponding to the front of the concert platform. The ripple patterns formed in the tank give a very good indication of the points in the hall where unwanted reflections will occur. If these are serious, the design may have to be modified.

The refinements in the acoustics will depend largely upon the interior decoration and furnishing of the hall. The use of carpets on the floors, of absorbent materials (*e.g.* plaster) on the walls and ceiling, and of suitably upholstered seats will help to put the finishing touches to satisfactory acoustic behaviour. The acoustic properties of the paint or other wall covering are at least as important

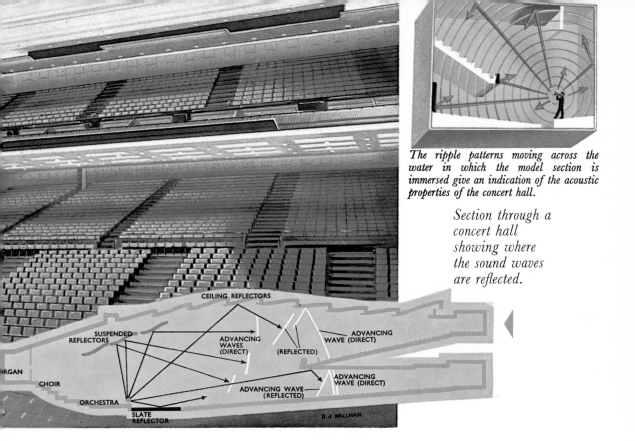

The ripple patterns moving across the water in which the model section is immersed give an indication of the acoustic properties of the concert hall.

Section through a concert hall showing where the sound waves are reflected.

CEILING REFLECTORS

SUSPENDED REFLECTORS

ADVANCING WAVES (DIRECT)

(REFLECTED)

ADVANCING WAVE (DIRECT)

ORGAN

CHOIR

ADVANCING WAVE (DIRECT)

ADVANCING WAVE (REFLECTED)

ORCHESTRA

SLATE REFLECTOR

D.J.WALLMAN

as its decorative value.

Various reflectors and baffles may be attached to the walls and ceiling to turn the sound waves in the most desirable direction. It is often necessary to have reflectors above the platform to throw the sound out into the body of the hall. The presence of an audience has a considerable effect upon the acoustics of many concert halls as the members of the audience are themselves quite good absorbers of sound waves. In consequence, there are marked differencies in the quality of music played in a half empty hall and when every seat is filled. This particular problem has been largely overcome in a famous concert hall where the tip-up seats have been designed so that they have similar absorption properties to those of the audience who may occupy them.

The purpose of a building should be reflected in its acoustic properties. In a theatre a shorter reverberation time is necessary (i.e. the number of reflections must be kept to a minimum), if the audience is to hear clearly what is being said on the stage. In contrast, the slower mellow tones of church music require that the reverberation time of a cathedral may be made longer (6 or 8 sec.).

In conclusion, mention may be made of the Whispering Galleries such as that in St. Paul's Cathedral in London. It is, at first, surprising to find that it is possible to stand at one side of the circular gallery and to be able to hear someone whispering at the opposite side. It has been shown that the listener is at the focal point of a giant concave reflector and that all sound waves coming from the opposite side of the gallery are collected by the reflector and at the focal point they reinforce one another.

CHAPTER THIRTY-SEVEN

Döppler Effect

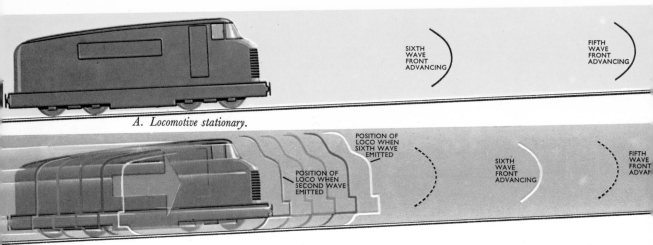

A. *Locomotive stationary.*

B. *Locomotive travelling at 90 m.p.h. towards observer.*

To a bystander a sudden lowering in pitch may be observed as an express train sounding its whistle travels at speed through a station. Likewise the tone of the engine of a fast moving sports car drops as it races by. In all these instances, the pitch of the sound is higher while the source of the sound is approaching the observer, but drops suddenly when it passes the observation point. Thus the pitch is lower when the source is travelling away.

This change in the pitch (or frequency) of a sound which results when a source of sound and its observer are moving *relative* to one another was first predicted by the Austrian physicist, C. J. Döppler in 1842. He showed that if the source was approaching the observer (or the observer was approaching the source) then the sound waves would be more crowded than if both the source and the observer were stationary.

A source of a certain steady fre-

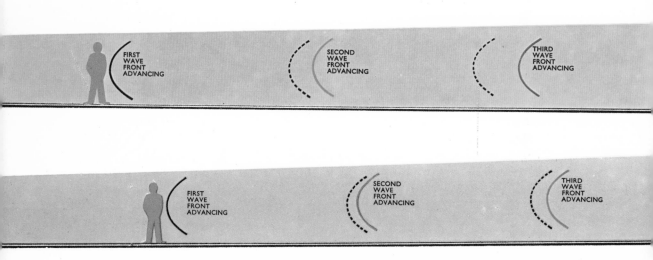

The whistle of the diesel locomotive is assumed to have a frequency of about 216 cycles per second (the wavelength of this sound is 5 feet). The four sketches show successive positions of the locomotive and the waves generated by the whistle at $\frac{1}{216}$ second intervals (i.e., corresponding positions of successive waves). The second sketch (B) shows that for a locomotive travelling towards an observer the distance between successive wave fronts is reduced. The third and fourth sketches (C and D) show how the distance between wave fronts is extended when the locomotive is going away from the observer.

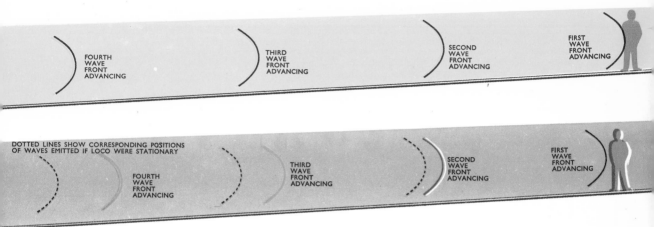

FOURTH WAVE FRONT ADVANCING

THIRD WAVE FRONT ADVANCING

SECOND WAVE FRONT ADVANCING

FIRST WAVE FRONT ADVANCING

DOTTED LINES SHOW CORRESPONDING POSITIONS OF WAVES EMITTED IF LOCO WERE STATIONARY

FOURTH WAVE FRONT ADVANCING

THIRD WAVE FRONT ADVANCING

SECOND WAVE FRONT ADVANCING

FIRST WAVE FRONT ADVANCING

quency n, will emit n complete sound waves (a series of push-and-pull changes in pressure) in one second. This is what is usually understood by frequency. If the source is stationary in relation to the observer, the observer's ears receive n sound waves in a second, so that the observer hears the actual sound that was given out by the source. However, if the source of sound is itself moving, this motion causes the air ahead of the source to be compressed by the vibrations

more than n times in a second, while the air behind the source is compressed less than n times in a second. As a consequence an observer in front of the approaching sound actually hears a sound of higher frequency, since more than n vibrations reach him in a second. After the source of sound has passed him the number of vibrations reaching him in a second is less than n so he hears a sound of lower pitch than the source.

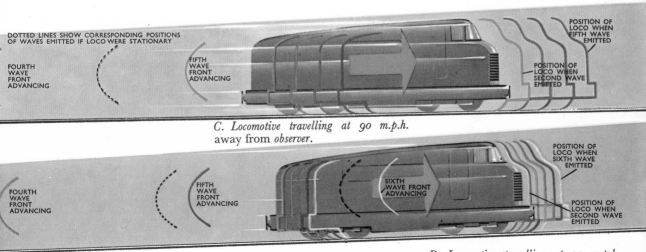

DOTTED LINES SHOW CORRESPONDING POSITIONS OF WAVES EMITTED IF LOCO WERE STATIONARY

FOURTH WAVE FRONT ADVANCING

FIFTH WAVE FRONT ADVANCING

POSITION OF LOCO WHEN FIFTH WAVE EMITTED

POSITION OF LOCO WHEN SECOND WAVE EMITTED

C. Locomotive travelling at 90 m.p.h.
away from observer.

FOURTH WAVE FRONT ADVANCING

FIFTH WAVE FRONT ADVANCING

SIXTH WAVE FRONT ADVANCING

POSITION OF LOCO WHEN SIXTH WAVE EMITTED

POSITION OF LOCO WHEN SECOND WAVE EMITTED

D. Locomotive travelling at 30 m.p.h.
away from observer.

CHAPTER THIRTY-EIGHT

The Velocity of Sound

THERE is something fascinating about listening to an echo. Most people like to hear their voices travelling across a valley, bouncing off a cliff and back to them. The sound of the voice travels with the speed of sound in air – about 750 miles per hour.

A sound wave is a variation in pressure which travels away from a vibrating source. The velocity of sound is important because it is a measure of the shortest time in which a pressure change can be transmitted from place to place. Compressional waves in solids and liquids are also called sound waves.

Measuring the Speed of Sound in Air

Early methods of finding the velocity of sound in air used cannon. An observer stood on a hill and timed the interval between the flash and hearing the report. Knowing the distance of the cannon, the velocity of the sound could

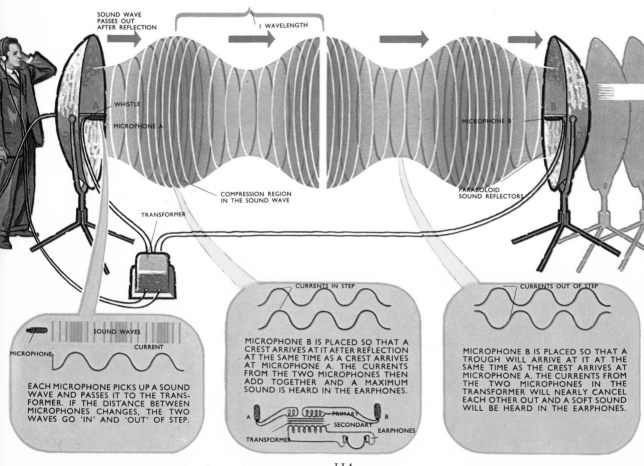

SOUND WAVE PASSES OUT AFTER REFLECTION

I WAVELENGTH

WHISTLE

MICROPHONE A

MICROPHONE B

COMPRESSION REGION IN THE SOUND WAVE

PARABOLOID SOUND REFLECTORS

TRANSFORMER

SOUND WAVES

CURRENT

MICROPHONE

CURRENTS IN STEP

CURRENTS OUT OF STEP

EACH MICROPHONE PICKS UP A SOUND WAVE AND PASSES IT TO THE TRANS-FORMER. IF THE DISTANCE BETWEEN MICROPHONES CHANGES, THE TWO WAVES GO 'IN' AND 'OUT' OF STEP.

MICROPHONE B IS PLACED SO THAT A CREST ARRIVES AT IT AFTER REFLECTION AT THE SAME TIME AS A CREST ARRIVES AT MICROPHONE A. THE CURRENTS FROM THE TWO MICROPHONES THEN ADD TOGETHER AND A MAXIMUM SOUND IS HEARD IN THE EARPHONES.

PRIMARY

SECONDARY

EARPHONES

TRANSFORMER

MICROPHONE B IS PLACED SO THAT A TROUGH WILL ARRIVE AT IT AT THE SAME TIME AS THE CREST ARRIVES AT MICROPHONE A. THE CURRENTS FROM THE TWO MICROPHONES IN THE TRANSFORMER WILL NEARLY CANCEL EACH OTHER OUT AND A SOFT SOUND WILL BE HEARD IN THE EARPHONES.

be calculated. This was not very accurate because the wind blew the sound away so that it had to travel in a curved path. Temperature variations in the air also caused it to refract away from a straight course.

The determination of the velocity of sound in the open was important for military reasons. It enabled artillery to be located. So in 1864 Charles Regnault decided to make a more accurate determination. He set up his equipment which used an electrical method to measure the time interval, in an underground pipe near Paris. The shot of the gun broke a circuit wire stretched across the muzzle and this moved an inked pen on a recording drum at the receiving end. When the sound arrived there it moved a diaphragm which marked the drum

again. Since the speed of rotation of the drum was known the velocity of sound could be found.

The velocity of sound is more accurately found by using two parabolic reflectors facing each other with a whistle of fixed frequency at the focus of one reflector. A microphone is placed beside the whistle and another microphone at the other focus and the leads from these two microphones are both connected to one side of a transformer. When earphones are connected up to the other side of the transformer, the output sound will grow louder and fainter as the reflectors are moved towards or away from each other. This is an example of interference in sound waves. When the sound in the earphones goes from a minimum to a maximum and back to

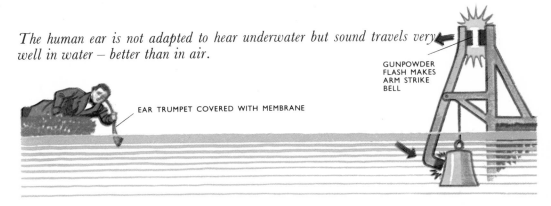

The human ear is not adapted to hear underwater but sound travels very well in water – better than in air.

GUNPOWDER FLASH MAKES ARM STRIKE BELL

EAR TRUMPET COVERED WITH MEMBRANE

OBSERVER TIMES INTERVAL BETWEEN SEEING FLASH AND HEARING CANNON.

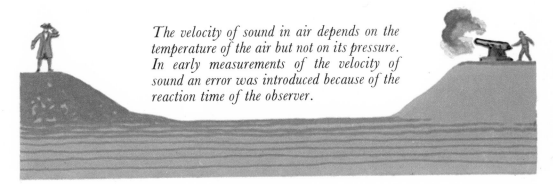

The velocity of sound in air depends on the temperature of the air but not on its pressure. In early measurements of the velocity of sound an error was introduced because of the reaction time of the observer.

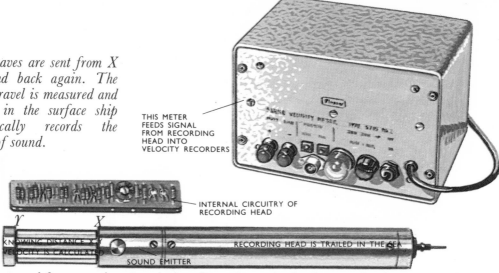

Sound waves are sent from X to Y and back again. The time of travel is measured and a meter in the surface ship automatically records the velocity of sound.

THIS METER FEEDS SIGNAL FROM RECORDING HEAD INTO VELOCITY RECORDERS

INTERNAL CIRCUITRY OF RECORDING HEAD

KNOWING DISTANCE XY VELOCITY IS CALCULATED

SOUND EMITTER

RECORDING HEAD IS TRAILED IN THE SEA

Instrument used for measuring the velocity of sound to a depth of 2,000 feet in the sea. The internal circuitry of the measuring head is shown.

a minimum, one reflector will have moved through exactly one wavelength. Knowing the frequency, one can calculate the speed of sound. This is an accurate, compact method and can be used also for ultrasonic sound waves.

Measuring the Velocity of Sound in Water

Lake Geneva was the site of the first measurement of the velocity of sound in water. A large bell under the surface was struck at the same time as a gunpowder charge was ignited above. This enabled an observer using a bent eartrumpet covered with a membrane in the water, to time the interval between the flash and hearing the bell. A large stretch of water was needed because the velocity of sound in water is nearly a mile a second.

It is important to have an accurate value of the velocity of sound in water in order to design echo-sounding apparatus. Present methods use the explosion of charges coinciding with a radio signal. The arrival of the sound is detected by *hydrophones* (underwater microphones) and the time interval

measured.

Sound does not die away so rapidly in water as in air and travels much further. Because of this it is possible to hear the sound of ships' propellers underwater, 8 to 10 miles away.

Variations in the Velocity

Like light, sound can be refracted. The sound alters speed as it passes from one material to another and refraction takes place at the boundary. Because of this it can be brought to a focus by a lens, not a glass lens, but a balloon lens filled with carbon dioxide.

Sound travels faster in warmer air than colder air and this can lead to *zones of silence*. The sound of an ammunition factory which blew up in Holland in 1923 was heard at various distances up to 500 miles, but was not heard in the interval between 60 and 100 miles. This was because the sound wave which had travelled along the ground had died away, and the sound being heard at greater distances was brought about by a sound wave which had gone up into the atmosphere and been refracted down by warmer air.

116

CHAPTER THIRTY-NINE

Measurement of Sound and Noise

VERY little energy is required to produce sound, and it is also transmitted very easily through the air, through building structures, or round corners.

A part of an engine or any vibrating object will be a source of sound, as it pulls and pushes the molecules of air around it. In air, as in other materials such as steel or concrete, these pressure variations, passed from one layer to the next, constitute a sound wave.

It is the variation in pressure of the air, caused by the arrival of a sound wave, that is commonly measured by scientists. Such measurements provide

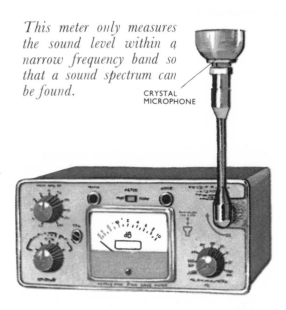

This meter only measures the sound level within a narrow frequency band so that a sound spectrum can be found.

CRYSTAL MICROPHONE

Ordinary sounds and the regions of intensity and frequency in which they lie. The diagram also shows the 'thresholds' of hearing and pain for human ears.

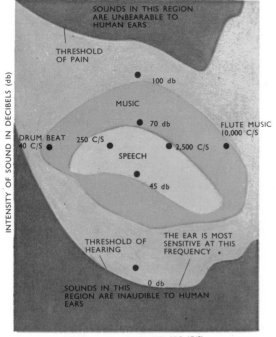

INTENSITY OF SOUND IN DECIBELS (db)

SOUNDS IN THIS REGION ARE UNBEARABLE TO HUMAN EARS

THRESHOLD OF PAIN

100 db

MUSIC

70 db

FLUTE MUSIC 10,000 C/S

DRUM BEAT 40 C/S   250 C/S   2,500 C/S

SPEECH

45 db

THRESHOLD OF HEARING   THE EAR IS MOST SENSITIVE AT THIS FREQUENCY .

SOUNDS IN THIS REGION ARE INAUDIBLE TO HUMAN EARS

0 db

FREQUENCY IN CYCLES PER SEC (C/S)

values of *sound pressure*. Another important quantity is *sound intensity*. This is a measure of the *energy* that is carried by the sound wave. It is not the same as the sound pressure but the two quantities are related – the larger the pressure, the greater the intensity. A third quantity is the *loudness* of a sound. This quantity tells us how loud a sound *seems* to be, compared with a 'standard' sound of fixed intensity and frequency. The frequency of the standard has to be fixed because, to the ear, two sounds of equal intensity but different frequency appear to be of different loudness.

For this reason, when loudness is measured, the intensity of the unknown sound is always compared with the intensity of a 1,000 cycle note.

Hearing Sound

Our ears are not equally sensitive to sounds of different frequency. Low

Finding a sound spectrum

An aircraft engineer wants a sound recording of an engine. His purpose is to find out the components which are emitting sound. Each of these emits sound of a certain frequency depending on its natural rate of vibration. Either an instrument called a *frequency analyzer* is brought along to the engine, or else a good tape recording is taken of the sound and this is then analyzed in the laboratory. The frequency analyzer can be switched to amplify only sound within certain narrow frequency bands. Starting at the lowest sound, and working gradually up to the highest frequency of sound, a sound spectrum is obtained which shows the different levels of sound in each frequency band.

The natural rate of vibration of each individual part of the engine is then found. Comparing this with the sound spectrum, the engineer knows which are the noisiest parts. Modifications can then be made.

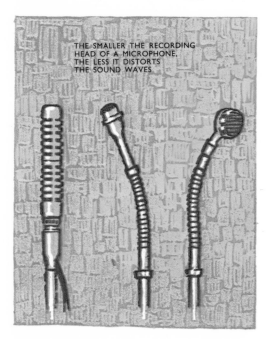

THE SMALLER THE RECORDING HEAD OF A MICROPHONE, THE LESS IT DISTORTS THE SOUND WAVES

notes and high notes do not seem as loud to us as notes of medium frequency. Our ears are most sensitive around 2,000 cycles per second. The lowest sound the ear hears is about 18 cycles per second and the highest about 18,000 cycles per second.

Measuring Sound – Rayleigh's Disc

There is a lower limit to the intensity of a note that we can hear. This varies with the frequency and is called the *threshold of hearing*. There is also an upper limit to the intensity we can hear. This also depends on frequency

and is called the *threshold of pain*.

If an elliptically shaped board is held at 45 degrees to the direction of a stream of air it will tend to set itself broadside on. This effect can be used to measure sound intensities. Similarly, if a small ellipse made of glass or mica is suspended by a fine stiff fibre at a fixed angle of 45 degrees in a sound wave, it will tend to set itself broadside on to the longitudinal back and forth motion of the air molecules. If a light beam is reflected off it, the

A Transistor sound level weighted meter which will read from 30 to 140 db.

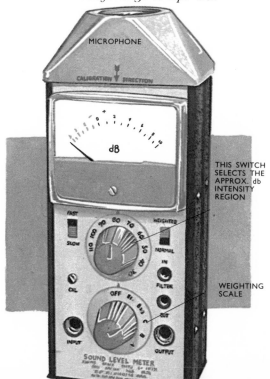

THIS SWITCH SELECTS THE APPROX. db INTENSITY REGION

WEIGHTING SCALE

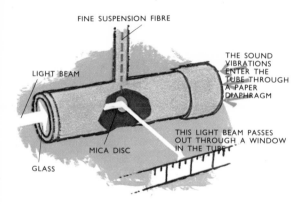

FINE SUSPENSION FIBRE

LIGHT BEAM

GLASS

MICA DISC

THE SOUND VIBRATIONS ENTER THE TUBE THROUGH A PAPER DIAPHRAGM

THIS LIGHT BEAM PASSES OUT THROUGH A WINDOW IN THE TUBE

A small elliptical shaped disc is deflected by a sound wave. This is called a Rayleigh Disc.

angle through which it turns can be noted and this is a measure of the intensity of the sound wave. This device is called a *Rayleigh disc*. Other types of mechanical instruments use a diaphragm which is set vibrating by the sound. The diaphragm moves a needle or reflects a beam of light on to a film and a record of the sound is made.

Electric sound-measuring instruments

Most electric sound-measuring instruments measure the sound *pressure*. These instruments are made up of a microphone, an amplifier, and some sort of recorder. In the microphone the sound pressure is converted into an electrical signal, which is amplified, and then used to operate a pen or a meter.

When the level of sound is measured (for example by public authorities whose job it is to control noise) it is important not only that the measurement should be accurate, but that the result should tell the operator how the sound would seem to the human ear. Because sounds of different frequencies but similar pressures do not seem equally loud to the ear, a device has been built into meters used for measuring sound pressure levels. This ensures that low sounds of equal pressures do not measure as loud as sounds of medium frequency (to which the ear is more sensitive). This is called *weighting* the frequency range. It is an attempt to approximate to the peculiarities of the human ear.

Measuring Loudness

The *equivalent loudness* instrument measures *loudness* and not sound *pressure*. It emits a note of 1,000 cycles per second which is heard in one ear through an earphone. The sound being measured is heard in the other ear, and the intensity of the 1,000 cycles per second note is adjusted until the two sounds seem of equal loudness.

Difficulty in measuring sound

The difficulty in measuring sound is that any instrument used will distort the sound wave and not give a true value. For this reason the receiving part of the instrument must be made very small. This is why the receiving heads of microphones are made as small as possible. If the person recording the sound is near, then he will also be a cause of distortion. This applies both to the microphones used for recording sound, and to sound-measuring instruments.

Exact sound measurements on an engine are best taken where there are no disturbing sound reflections. This can be in the open air, where the microphone is enclosed in a silken balloon to remove wind effects, or in an *anechoic chamber* that is, a room designed to be without echoes. But for ordinary measurement of background noise such as from traffic or office typewriters, only the general level of sound, including echoes, is measured.

Supersonic Bangs

A MOVING aircraft flies over an observer watching it from the ground. If it is flying faster than the speed of sound, the observer does not hear it approach him. Not until *after* the aircraft has passed overhead does he hear it. Then a short time later come two violent, window-shattering *supersonic bangs*.

The bangs always occur whenever an aircraft 'breaks the sound barrier'. Although the violence of the bang depends on a great many things, a loud disturbance is absolutely unavoidable. No amount of streamlining eliminates it completely.

The aircraft disturbs the air through which it passes. When it is moving at a speed greater than the speed of sound, it is moving faster than the disturbance it creates. So the disturbance *follows* the aircraft, and takes the form of two *shock waves*, one at the nose and the other at the tail of the aircraft.

Ideally, at all speeds, the aircraft

Shock waves form the surfaces of two cones, one stretching from the nose and the other from the tail of the aircraft. The two men on the ground hear the bangs when the shock waves hit the ground.

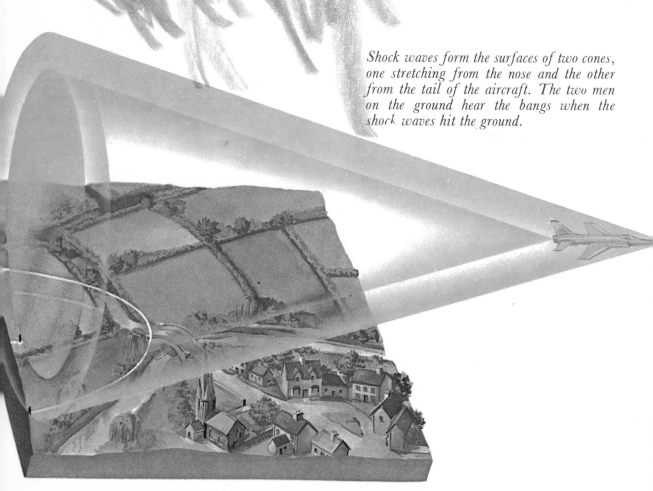

These diagrams show how the movement of a source of sound waves affects the way they travel. The sound waves coming from a stationary source spread out equally in all directions. Each diagram shows the wave an instant later than in the previous diagram.

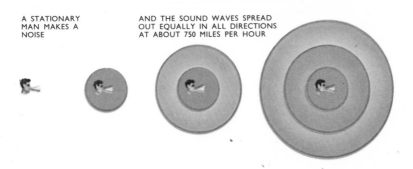

A STATIONARY MAN MAKES A NOISE

AND THE SOUND WAVES SPREAD OUT EQUALLY IN ALL DIRECTIONS AT ABOUT 750 MILES PER HOUR

should gently part the air, and the air should stream smoothly around the fuselage. But always, ahead of the nose of the aircraft, the air will be compressed, and just behind the tail, it will be rarified. This happens however perfect the streamlining.

The pressure disturbances at the nose and tail are the same kind of thing as sound disturbances.

Sounds are very weak pressure variations, and in air under normal conditions of temperature and pressure, they travel away from their source at about 750 miles per hour. Any pressure disturbance spreads out from its source in all directions.

Similarly the compression of the air at the nose of the aircraft spreads out from the nose in all directions.

A moving aircraft causes a pressure disturbance as it pushes air apart. The aircraft is now travelling at less than the speed of sound. The disturbances made by the aircraft in each successive instant are moved, with the aircraft, to the right. This distorts the shape of the wave.

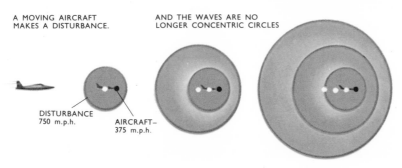

A MOVING AIRCRAFT MAKES A DISTURBANCE.

AND THE WAVES ARE NO LONGER CONCENTRIC CIRCLES

DISTURBANCE 750 m.p.h.

AIRCRAFT– 375 m.p.h.

Now the aircraft is travelling faster than sound. In other words it is travelling ahead of its disturbance. In this example, the aircraft is travelling at Mach 2 (twice the speed of sound). In each instant, the aircraft travels twice as far as the disturbance. The shape of the shock wave now becomes apparent. It is the line (or in three dimensions, the surface) dividing the region which has received the disturbance from the region which has not. Because the air ahead is not forewarned of the coming disturbance, it arrives suddenly, in a shock wave.

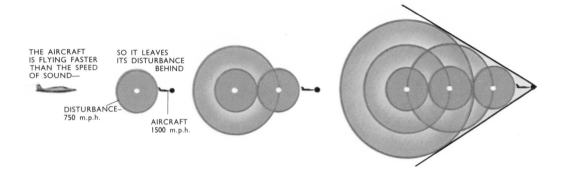

THE AIRCRAFT IS FLYING FASTER THAN THE SPEED OF SOUND—

SO IT LEAVES ITS DISTURBANCE BEHIND

DISTURBANCE— 750 m.p.h.

AIRCRAFT 1500 m.p.h.

When the aircraft is moving forward, the movement distorts the *resultant* direction of travel of the disturbance (this is the direction which would be noted by a stationary observer). Provided the aircraft is travelling at less than the speed of sound, the disturbance can travel ahead of the aircraft. It is as if the air is forewarned of the coming of the aircraft, and it has time to start to get out of the way before the aircraft actually reaches it.

But as the aircraft accelerates, and flies faster than sound, the disturbances cannot get away. The air ahead has no advance warning that the aircraft is coming, and it must therefore part *abruptly*. The sudden parting forms a 'wave' of suddenly-compressed air, the shock wave.

At the tail of the aircraft the air suddenly meets again, after being parted by the aircraft. This causes a pressure disturbance in the air which cannot be transmitted forwards. So, again, the air ahead is not forewarned

and the sudden jump in pressure forms the tail 'wave' where the pressure alters rapidly.

The shock waves can be thought of as barriers of tightly compressed air. But the aircraft never 'breaks' the barrier. No matter how many times faster than sound it travels, the shock waves remain intact. The phrase 'breaking the sound barrier' means travelling faster than sound, but no actual physical barrier is broken.

The shocks spread out from the nose and tail ends like the waves which spread out from the bow and stern of a ship. The shock travels to the observer with the speed of sound, and he interprets the sudden violent change of pressure as an ear-drum-shattering bang. He hears two shock waves, one spreading out from the nose, and the other spreading out from the tail. These follow one another in rapid succession.

In most aircraft, there will be more than two shock waves. Shock waves may form at wing tips, or at any other point on the aircraft where the air-flow is parted. In supersonic aircraft the wings are swept back so that the wing tips lie inside the nose and tail shock waves. Because the stream-line flow around it has been disturbed, the aircraft may be subjected to consider-able buffeting. Modern design has largely eliminated this.

To hear the supersonic bangs, the observer must be standing within a certain area. This can be worked out from the geometry of the situation. The shock waves form two cones, with their pointed ends at the nose and the tail. The supersonic bang can be heard by someone standing on the ground on the curved lines where the cones meet the ground. While the air-craft moves forward, this line sweeps out an area. Inside the area, the observer will hear the two consecu-tive bangs. Outside it, he hears nothing.

Supersonic bangs do not annoy the people travelling in the aircraft, for the shock waves do not reach them. They can, however, be very disturbing to people and property on the ground. So it is important to restrict the extent of the bangs, particularly in the vicinity of airports used by super-sonic airliners. The bangs can be heard only within a certain area, the size of which depends on several things – the speed of the aircraft rela-tive to the speed of sound (the *Mach number*), the height of the aircraft, whether it is climbing, in level flight, or diving, and the way the tempera-ture varies in the atmosphere between it and the ground. All these are signi-ficant factors which may influence the location and design of supersonic airports.

The faster the aircraft travels, the more pointed become its shock-wave cones. The shape of the cone can be found by drawing in spheres to represent the disturbance after each instant.

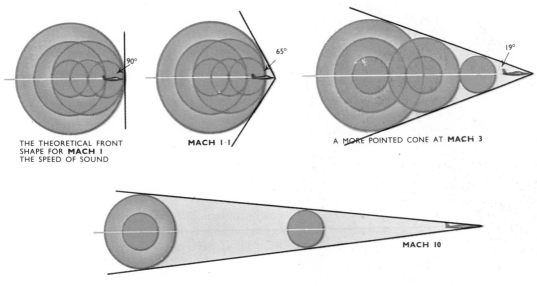

THE THEORETICAL FRONT SHAPE FOR **MACH 1** THE SPEED OF SOUND

MACH 1·1

A MORE POINTED CONE AT **MACH 3**

MACH 10

CHAPTER FORTY-ONE

Ultrasonics

THE human ear is not built to detect waves which vibrate less than about 20 times per second (*i.e.* have a frequency of less than 20 cycles per second) or more than about 20,000 times a second. Waves whose frequencies are greater than this are called *ultrasonic*.

A taut piece of elastic vibrates if

An ultrasonic plant for cleaning cutlery. This equipment can clean knives and forks in 20 seconds.

it is struck, and the disturbance created by the vibration forms sound waves in the air around. The frequency of the note depends on the thickness, length and tautness of the elastic, and it will probably be in the audible region. Ultrasonic waves, however, cannot conveniently be made by this method. The vibrating part is instead a piece of crystal – quartz or Rochelle Salt, or specially made ceramic crystals, such as barium titanate. These crystals can vibrate only at certain, very precisely defined frequencies, which depend on the size and shape of the crystal, and the way it is held and forced to vibrate. If the crystal is struck it will vibrate, but these vibrations soon die down. The special property of these crystals, which are called *piezo-electric*, is that they can be made to vibrate, to and fro, by giving them a to-and-fro *electrical* impulse. An electric current can be made to alternate, to and fro, fairly easily with an *oscillator*. The crystal is sandwiched between two metal plates, and the alternating electric current connected to the plates. Provided the electric current is alternating at one of the frequencies allowed by the crystal, the crystal will vibrate and continue to vibrate.

Piezo-electric crystals happen to vibrate at ultrasonic frequencies, ranging from about 20,000 cycles per second to several million cycles per second. They can make strong ultrasonic waves, and concentrate the energy of the wave into a very narrow beam. These properties lead to their use in *echo-sounding*. A vibrating crystal (called a *transducer*) sends a narrow beam of ultrasonic waves from the surface to the depths of the ocean, and this beam is *reflected* by the ocean bed, or by anything else, for example a shoal of fish or a submarine, which happens to lie in between. The time the beam takes to return (i.e. the returning beam is the 'echo') is a measure of the depth of the fish, or the ocean bed. Ordinary sound waves would soon be scattered in travelling through the water.

Ultrasonic waves are now being used in a useful form of echo-sounding on a smaller scale. The waves can be made to pass through solid substances, but the way in which they travel naturally depends on the nature of the substance. If there are 'breaks' in the solid, or boundaries between one solid and another, these will show up on the ultrasonic 'trace', as more waves are reflected from one part than another. Aluminium castings for use in aircraft, for instance, must have

An aluminium aircraft forging being 'echo-sounded' with an ultrasonic hand-probe.

no structural defects, since these would tend to extend and give way when the fuselage is under pressure. So every inch is tested ultrasonically. Stray 'echoes' picked up by the tester may mean a break in the structure of the metal.

In some kinds of ultrasonic testing, the vibration of the crystal is *coupled* to the solid under test by a thin layer of oil. The crystal makes the oil vibrate and the oil in turn makes the solid vibrate. The whole of the solid can be tested if it is completely immersed in a liquid bath. A beam of ultrasonic waves directed at the solid is rather like a beam of X-rays. It can pass through some parts of the solid more easily than others, to give an ultrasonic 'picture' of the solid. Unlike X-rays, ultrasonic waves have no harmful effect on most kinds of living tissues, and ultrasonic 'photographs' may replace X-rays as a means of diagnosing ill-

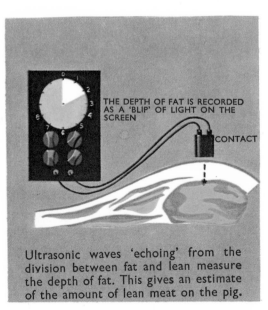

THE DEPTH OF FAT IS RECORDED AS A 'BLIP' OF LIGHT ON THE SCREEN

CONTACT

Ultrasonic waves 'echoing' from the division between fat and lean measure the depth of fat. This gives an estimate of the amount of lean meat on the pig.

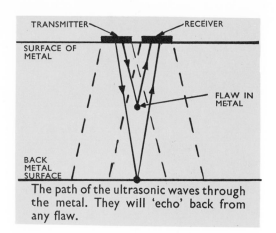

The path of the ultrasonic waves through the metal. They will 'echo' back from any flaw.

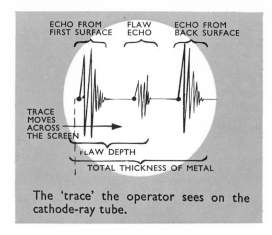

The 'trace' the operator sees on the cathode-ray tube.

nesses. The patient must, however, sit in a bath while he is being 'sounded' so that the crystal vibrations can be transferred to his body.

Normally the only way we can 'feel' sound waves is by the delicate detecting mechanism in the ear. This is because the actual disturbance of the air is very small indeed. As the air moves slightly to and fro, its *pressure* increases and decreases (the to-and-fro movements alternately compress and rarefy the air), and it is the slight pressure changes which the ear detects. Similarly if the ear is immersed in water, it can hear the pressure changes caused by a sound wave in the water. Although the molecules of air or water move only about a millionth of an inch, they move far farther than the molecules of a vibrating solid. The difference between the movement of different kinds of molecules under the same pressure wave is the basis of *ultrasonic cleaning*.

In washing-up or laundering the water needs to be agitated. This creates pressure waves in the liquid, and if the water is agitated violently enough, the waves can reach all parts of the washing. The pressure changes help

to remove the dirt from the washing. But these pressure changes need to be fairly violent to be effective, and they may damage delicate fabrics. The cleaning action is better and gentler if the waves are ultrasonic. A pressure wave in a liquid acts on any solid like a succession of sucks and blows. At the 'suck' liquid molecules move away from the solid. But solid molecules, since they are bound to the solid, cannot follow. So a tiny 'bubble' of vacuum is made on the surface of the solid. Any dirt on its surface is pulled off to try to fill the vacuum, and the dirt is shot away as the bubble 'bursts'. Ultrasonic cleaning is used in industry to clean delicate components, such as the parts of a watch, or to speed up cleaning of more robust objects. It can clean completely and thoroughly in about 20 seconds.

The cleaning action is 'safe' only if the substance can withstand the 'sucking' of the tiny bubbles. Ultrasonic waves have been found to kill small living organisms such as algae or bacteria, by puncturing the walls of their cells. This method is in fact being used by chemists as a means of breaking down large molecules into smaller ones.

Index